SECOND WORLD WAR STORIES FOR BOYS

J. ELDRIDGE

For my grandsons, Jack & Albert; with love from Grandad Jim

While the events described and some of the characters in this book may be based on actual historical events and real people, the main characters in these stories are fictional, created by the author, and their stories are works of fiction.

Scholastic Children's Books
Euston House, 24 Eversholt Street,
London, NW1 1DB, UK
A division of Scholastic Ltd

London ~ New York ~ Toronto ~ Sydney ~ Auckland
Mexico City ~ New Delhi ~ Hong Kong

First published in the UK as three separate titles (*Deadly Skies*, *Tank Attack* and *Behind Enemy Lines*) in the Warpath series by Puffin, 1999
First published in this format in the UK by Scholastic Ltd, 2012

ISBN 978 1407 13227 3

Printed and bound in the UK by CPI Group (UK) Ltd, Croydon, CR0 4YY

2 4 6 8 10 9 7 5 3

DEADLY SKIES

INVASION BRITAIN

The attacks by the German Forces at the start of World War Two had been swift and decisive. By May 1940 they had swept through most of northern Europe: Denmark, Norway, Belgium, Luxembourg, Holland and France. The BEF (British Expeditionary Force) sent to try to stop Hitler's advancing armies were defeated, and 340,000 soldiers (mostly British) were evacuated from the French seaport of Dunkirk during the end of May and the start of June by a flotilla of boats.

Less than a year since Britain had declared war on Germany, in September 1939, it looked as if Hitler's ambition to conquer Europe was almost complete. Only one country remained unconquered: Britain – separated from mainland Europe by a narrow strip of water, the English Channel.

Even in 1940, Britain was still poorly prepared for war, lacking the necessary weapons and resources to defend itself against a strong invader. By July 1940, the German plans for the invasion of Britain were ready.

A series of attacks which would destroy the RAF were to be mounted by the Luftwaffe. Without the RAF there would be no air cover to defend Britain against a sea invasion. This operation – code-named "Sea Lion" – was to take place on 15 September. German forces superior both in numbers and armaments would then cross the Channel and invade Britain. With Britain defeated, the war in Europe would effectively be over. However, the whole operation depended on the destruction of the RAF prior to the invasion starting. Hitler knew this only too well, the opening paragraph of his own directive to his commanders of 1 August said: "Using all possible means, the German air forces will smash the British air forces in as brief a period of time as possible."

With a Luftwaffe air fleet of 3,000 German planes against 620 RAF Spitfires and Hurricanes, and only a thousand trained pilots to fly those few planes, the scene was set for a fateful encounter in the deadly skies over Southern England. It was to be a battle neither side could afford to lose.

PILOT'S KIT LIST

Helmets - made of brown leather, with telephone earpieces in zipped padded oval housings. The helmet had a chamois leather lining, a chinstrap and a slit back with adjustment strap, which acted as a quick release to pull off the helmet and oxygen mask from the pilot's head in the event of bailing out.

Goggles - a split-window mask made of celluloid with either brass Bakelite surround. Rubber padding surrounded the goggles.

Oxygen masks - fitted with an in-built microphone. Two types were in use during the Battle of Britain: Type C carbon microphone and Type 19 electromagnetic.

Gloves and gauntlets - inner gloves were made of silk and chamois, with woollen fingerless mitts on top, and brown leather outer gauntlets over that. Gloves were essential because warm hands were needed for careful flying and weapons' use.

Flying boots - either the 1930 pattern: made of chestnut sheepskin with front zip fastening and a strap at the top, or the 1936 pattern: straight pull-on black leather with a fleecy lining and with a tightening strap at the top.

Life jackets - 1932 pattern: a thick khaki cotton twill waistcoat closed with three buttons and two buckled straps, housing a bladder (inflated by mouth). It was painted yellow to make the wearer more visible when in the sea.

Parachute

Under Attack

"Green Leader to Green 3, see anything yet, Bonzo?"

"Green 3 to Green Leader. Nothing yet, skipper."

"Radar says they're on their way. Keep 'em peeled."

Green 3. That was me, John "Bonzo" Smith. Nineteen years old. Third pilot in Green Section of 327 Fighter Squadron. Ian "Tug" Banks was our immediate skipper; our Section Leader, Charlie "Dob" Masters, was Green 2, the other pilot in our wing of three.

327 Squadron flew in three V-formations of three planes each: Red Section, Blue Section and Green Section.

We'd been scrambled from our base in Hornchurch, Essex, just five minutes before when our radar had warned that the Luftwaffe was on its way. Now we flew over the countryside of north Kent, just to the south and east of London. Below me I could see the mudflats of the Thames Estuary, the river now wide and becoming sea, cold and blue, so very different from the brown river that snaked through London.

"Still no sign."

"Let's take a stroll and see what we can find," came the voice of Jerry Payne, the leader of Red Section, in my headphones.

He took a turn to the right, and one by one each section followed him, spreading out so that we patrolled the east Kent area in a line formation.

I was relatively new to Spitfires. I'd joined 327 Squadron just two months earlier after my training, most of which had been done on Tiger Moths and Miles Masters. Compared to the Tiger and the Miles, the Spitfire seemed much more cramped, with its long narrow cockpit, but I soon learned the value of it. The narrower Spitfire was able to turn much quicker and get you out of trouble when under attack.

It was able to twist and turn, loop and dive in a short arc, providing you could take the strain that came with a sudden loss of gravity as you dived, or increased pressure as you went into a rapid climb. Even now, after two months, I still felt a sense of excitement and amazement that I, Bonzo Smith, was actually at the controls of a Spitfire – the best fighter plane in the whole world!

Suddenly I saw the German planes about half a mile ahead of us and closing, at 17,00 feet: sixteen Messerschmitt 109s, instantly recognizable by their yellow nose-tips, flying in the German "finger-four" formations.

"Here we go!" came Red Leader's voice over my radio-telephone. "Battle formations."

"Green Section, line astern!" ordered Tug.

Dob and I brought our Spitfires into line behind Tug's plane. Then Tug dropped his nose and dived, while Dob and I soared up. As we'd hoped, the leading Messerschmitt went down after our leader, guns blazing, but Tug had already hauled back on his own controls hard and was now soaring upwards, at the same time turning to the right. The Messerschmitt pilot attempted to follow Tug, still firing, but his manoeuvre now brought him into my range. I kicked my rudder to the right, kept my gunsights ahead of him, then turned the gun button to "Fire" and let go with a three-second burst. The bullets from all of my eight guns hit him, raking the aircraft from nose to tail. A burst of flame shot upwards, and then the Messerschmitt spun away downwards, black smoke pouring from its engine.

"Bandits behind you, Green 3!" Dob shouted in my headphones. I instinctively pushed the joystick forward and went into a dive, turning as I went. The plane shuddered as a tracer of bullets tore into my fuselage. I pulled back hard in a steep climb until I completed a loop, which brought me on the tail of my opponent. He must have been expecting my move because he rolled to one side, just as I fired, and my bullets narrowly missed him.

"Blast!" I scowled.

"Better shooting next time, Bonzo!" laughed Tug.

By now the sky was filled with thin lines of white smoke from planes as they looped and turned in the air. There were thicker lines of black smoke from those that had been hit.

Above the sound of the dogfighting I heard the drone of heavy aero-engines getting nearer. I put my Spitfire into a level flight heading out towards the sea and saw them emerging from the clouds: a fleet of Heinkel-111 bombers with their Messerschmitt 109 escorts flying close at 13,000 feet. This was the real attack force, the first wave of Messerschmitts had been to clear the way for the main bombing attack.

"Heinkels at twelve o'clock!" I barked into my radio-telephone.

The rest of the squadron had already seen them and were quickly turning to attack.

Tug took his Spitfire to 14,000 feet, about 1,000 feet above the approaching Heinkels. Dob and I followed him, flying now in a V-formation, keeping to one side and just behind him. We flew over the first Heinkels, leaving them to Red Section, which was now just behind us.

There was a chance the new wave of Messerschmitts might break away and attack us, but luckily they were sticking close to their Heinkels in their role of protectors, which meant their speed was limited to just over 200 miles an hour instead of their usual 330 mph.

"Going in!" said Tug's voice in my earphones.

He swooped down on the nearest Messerschmitt, firing all the while. The Messerschmitt pilot went into an upward climb, trying to get above Tug's tracer fire. Tug followed him, flying higher in a circular movement. This left the Heinkel's right side exposed, and Dob went in, all guns firing. The machine-gunner positioned at the top of the bomber saw Dob coming and let fly with a tracer of bullets. Dob swerved just in time to miss them, and then went into a dive, trying to come up under the bomber, but the Heinkel's machine-gunner in the "dustbin bay" beneath the plane started firing, trying to get a fix on him. For a second, while both machine-gunners in the body of the plane were distracted, I had a chance, and I took it. I banked and then came in fast just above the Heinkel, dropped my nose a fraction, and then let go with a two-second burst into the dome of the cockpit. I saw the glass shatter as my bullets tore into it, and then I was flying past and ahead. I turned sharply and then headed straight back for it. The front of the Heinkel was a mess, the machine gun in the nose was out of action, but she was still keeping on course. I managed to get another burst off and then abruptly changed course to fly straight over and along it. The bottom of my plane barely missed the top of the large bomber.

I banked, preparing to come in for a third time, but there was no need. The Heinkel was already spiralling out of control, flames flickering along the fuselage.

That's one German bomber than won't be doing any more damage, I thought to myself, deeply satisfied.

Suddenly I felt a massive THUMP, and then an explosion knocked the controls out of my hands. The Spitfire dropped and the cockpit began to fill with smoke. Flames licked around my feet. As I plunged towards the ground I could feel myself starting to lose consciousness. Smoke had now filled the cockpit; I couldn't see anything or scarcely breathe. I didn't know if I was over land or sea. I didn't know my altitude; all I knew for certain was that I'd been hit and was trapped inside a burning plane.

I tried to force the cockpit hood back, but it was stuck. The smoke had now blinded me completely. I knew I only had a few more seconds before the smoke overwhelmed me and the plane smashed into the ground.

I undid my safety belt, lifted myself up and hit the cockpit hood with all my strength … and as if by a miracle this time it gave way and flew off. I grabbed the side of the cockpit opening and pushed myself out.

For a few seconds I fell through open sky, my burning Spitfire spiralling downwards beneath me, before I pulled my ripcord and the parachute opened above me.

I looked down, and the green fields below, previously so far away, now rushed up to meet me.

As the wind swept me in I pulled on one side of the parachute, aiming clear of the line of trees that formed the boundary between two fields. I hit the ground and rolled over, and then staggered back to my feet again as the parachute billowed down to the ground around me. Above me, the air battle still raged. But I was alive. Then a voice behind me shouted, "Put your hands up! Make one false move and you're dead!"

Landed

I raised my hands and turned round to find myself face to face with a pitchfork. Behind it stood a large, elderly man dressed in farm labourer's clothes.

"Got you, you German spy!" scowled the man.

"German?!" I gaped. Then I laughed. "Do I look like or sound like a German?"

"Spies don't," said the man. "But you can't fool me!"

There was the sound of running feet in a nearby field and a voice called out, "Put that thing down, Joe, you idiot! He's one of ours!"

I saw another elderly man rush through a gap in a nearby hedge. With him were two children, a boy and girl. They made their way over to me as I disentangled myself from my parachute. Joe lowered the pitchfork, but he still glared at me suspiciously.

The man who'd just arrived came up to me, shook my hand vigorously, beaming all the while.

"I'm sorry about that," he said. "Joe's been told so often to watch out for invading Germans he's taken it a bit too seriously. My name's Josh Poole. This is my farm and these are my grandchildren, William and Carol. Are you OK?"

"Fine, thanks," I said. "Just a bit shaken up."

The two children were still looking at me goggle-eyed, as if I was a man from outer space.

"I knew you were one of ours," said William. "I've got pictures of all the uniforms. That was a Spitfire you were flying, wasn't it?"

I nodded. "Not much left of it now, though I'm afraid," I said ruefully.

"We'll talk later," said Mr Poole. "You'd better come up to the farmhouse and have a cup of tea. You'll feel better after that."

"I need to get a message to my base and let them know I'm all right," I said. "Is there a telephone near here?"

"We've got one at the farm," said Mr Poole. "And we'll see what the wife can rustle up for you in the way of food. I expect you're hungry after all that air-battling up there."

"It's called dogfighting, Grandad," explained William. "Isn't it?" he said to me.

I nodded, and added with a grin: "Though frankly most dogs are too clever to want to go up in a plane and do that sort of thing."

We walked the mile or so across the fields to the Pooles' farmhouse. Now that Joe was convinced I wasn't a German, he insisted on carrying my parachute for me, despite my protests that I could carry it myself.

We got back to the farmhouse, where Mr Poole spent about five minutes trying to get hold of the operator. Finally I was able to get a message back to my base at Hornchurch. I told them I was OK and would be back as soon as I could. Afterwards they sat me down at the table in the large warm kitchen and Mrs Poole handed me a huge plate of eggs and bacon and a big mug of steaming hot tea. I sat and ate hungrily, though it was hard to be completely relaxed about it because of everyone staring at me, in particular Joe and the two children. I must have been the first flyer they'd seen close up, and with all my gear on I must have cut an unusual figure for them.

"Have you been flying Spitfires long?" asked William, keen to find out more about his favourite plane.

"Where's Hornchurch?" asked Carol, who'd been listening as I'd made my telephone call.

"Let the poor young man eat his meal," said Mrs Poole.

"Too many questions," muttered Joe darkly. "Careless talk costs lives."

"Joe's one of our keenest Home Guard members," explained Mr Poole. "He takes the orders he's given by our local captain very seriously."

"Jerry won't invade while I'm around!" nodded Joe confidently.

As I ate I listened and got the picture: Mr Poole and Joe

were both in the local unit of the Home Guard, Britain's last line of defence.

William and Carol were keen to talk about the war: how many German planes I'd shot down; did I think it would last long, all those sorts of questions.

"I hope it goes on for a bit longer," said William.

"That's a terrible thing to say, William," said his grandmother. "Think of all those more people getting killed every day it goes on."

"Yes, but I want to fight, too," said William, "and I can't fight until I'm older."

"With a bit of luck it'll all be over by Christmas," said Mr Poole. "If you ask me, Hitler's overstretched himself, rushing through Europe as fast as he did."

"That's what they said last autumn," said Mrs Poole soberly. "They said it was all going to be over by last Christmas. If you ask me, this war'll go on and on. Just like the last one."

"I'll do my best to make it as short as I can," I threw in, trying to make as light of it as I could.

The clock on the mantelpiece chimed, and I realized I'd been sitting here in this comfortable farmhouse, so near yet so far from the war, eating and chatting for an hour, and I suddenly felt guilty.

"I'd better be going," I said. "They'll be wondering what's

taking me so long. If you could run me to the nearest station…"

"Run you to the station?!" snorted Mr Poole. "Nonsense, I'll run you back to your base."

"But that's right on the other side of London!" I protested.

"You're fighting for us, putting your life at risk every time you go up in one of those things," said Mr Poole. "The least I can do is take you back to your base. Anyway, how would you get your parachute back without me taking you, and that's vital to the war effort, that is."

In the face of such determined kindness I could hardly refuse such an offer.

Mrs Poole had made me some sandwiches, which she wrapped in greaseproof paper and pressed into my hand as I got into Mr Poole's old car. Mrs Poole, the two children and Joe waved us goodbye as we drove away.

As we drove north through the Kent countryside, Mr Poole explained to me why William was so keen to join up and fight.

"His dad, our son, Timmy, was killed at Dunkirk. It hit William especially hard."

As we drove, Mr Poole talked about his son, Timmy, who never came back from the beach at Dunkirk. What a good farmer Timmy was. A hard worker. A good father. How much the future had held for him. All I could so was sit and listen, and sympathize, and promise that I would do my best to make sure that Timmy Poole hadn't died in vain.

By the time we got back to Hornchurch, darkness was starting to fall. Mr Poole let me off at the gate. I struggled out of his car with my loosely-packed parachute, shook him by the hand, and promised that after the war was over I'd call on him again at his farm, and next time the meal would be on me. Mr Poole gave me a broad smile before driving off into the night.

The first person I ran into as I walked back into the base was Flight Sergeant Pearson, or "Crusty" Pearson, so called because of his crusty ways, always finding fault with everything.

"Smith!" he barked. "Where have you been? On holiday?"

"Kent, sir," I said. "I did get a telephone message through. I was shot down and had to bail out."

"I know you were shot down," snapped Crusty. "You nearly got yourself killed. That wouldn't have done at all."

I was just starting to think that maybe Crusty had a warm heart underneath that tough exterior, when he spoilt it by adding: "We can't afford to lose a trained pilot. Nor can we afford to lose fighters. You blokes are losing planes faster than we can replace them. You're in trouble, Smith!"

Just my luck! I groaned to myself. Not only do I nearly get myself killed, now I'm going to be court-martialled for destroying RAF property!

As Crusty glowered at me, I decided I wasn't going to go down without a fight.

"I did shoot down two of theirs, sir," I pointed out. "Two for the price of one, so we showed a profit."

"We need a ratio of six to one to make a profit, five to one to break even," snapped Crusty. "We're outnumbered, remember?"

Tug Banks and Dob Masters had been watching this exchange and they came over to greet me as Crusty marched off.

When side by side, Tug and Dob always reminded me a little of Laurel and Hardy. Tug was quite small, thin and wiry, while Dob was tall and wide. Dob even had a moustache, small at the moment but one that he was growing into a handlebar-type.

"Return of the wandering hero," grinned Tug.

"How dare you upset poor kind-hearted Flight Sergeant Pearson," added Dob with a broad smile. "He only has your welfare at heart."

"Huh! Anyone would think they were his own private planes to hear him talk," I said, still feeling a bit sour about the way Crusty had told me off.

"Don't mind him, Bonzo," said Tug. "He's like that with everyone. I wrecked the first plane I ever took out, never even got off the ground with it. Put down the nose too sharply as I was taking off and somersaulted it." Tug laughed. "So next time Crusty moans at you if you lose a plane, tell him at least you got it off the ground, which was more than your Section Leader did."

"I don't intend to lose any more," I said confidently. "At least, not if I can help it."

"We're off to the mess for a cup of tea," said Dob. "Come and join us, but pick up your post first. There are a couple of letters for you."

They headed off for the mess, while I hurried to the post boxes in the Operations Hut to pick up my mail.

As Dob had said, there were two letters waiting for me. One was from my mother – I recognized her very tight handwriting on the envelope. The other was from my elder brother, Edward, and this was the one I opened first. Edward was fighting overseas and I was keen to hear how he was getting on.

Like the military man he was, Edward's letter gave nothing away: not even where abouts in the world he was. For all anyone else who read the letter could tell, Edward could have been in Africa or South America, although the word in the family was that he and his unit had been sent to Norway.

The letter had been written some weeks ago. As always, Edward's tone was cheerful, full of funny anecdotes about the trouble he had with finding bootlaces to fit, and wondering if a steel helmet was really that much defence if a bomb dropped directly on you. That was Edward's way, always making a joke of things. He ended: "Have you heard anything from Ma and Pa? If you see them, give them my love. I've dropped them a note, too, but with this war you never know if any of these letters are actually getting through."

Afterwards, I opened the letter from my mother. It was very short, not much news. They hadn't heard from Edward – though I guessed they would have by now. Father was well, though his leg was giving him trouble. They looked forward to seeing me when I got a chance for a spot of leave.

As luck would have it I was due for leave, and when I got to the mess to join Tug and Dob, Tug suggested I take it the next day.

"After all, we haven't got a plane for you at the moment. With a bit of luck your replacement kite should be here the day after tomorrow, so you might as well take tomorrow off and see your folks. The way Hitler's stepping up his air attacks there's no knowing when you'll get the chance for leave next."

Taking Tug's advice, I arranged a chit for Order of Leave, and next morning set off for my parents' house in London.

I got a lift to the station and travelled up to London by train. I needed the time on the train to think, prepare myself for the ordeal of visiting. That sounds a terrible thing to say when talking about visiting your own parents, but the truth was my father disapproved of me for joining the RAF. Pa had been a colonel in the Fusiliers in the First World War. That was where he'd received the injury to his leg, which kept him out of active service during this war. His father – my grandfather – had been in the same regiment, as had my great-grandfather before him. It had always been expected of me by my father that I would follow my brother, Edward, along the same route he'd taken, joining the Fusiliers – the family regiment, as Pa called it. We'd been a family of professional army men for generations – soldiers to the last. Instead I'd joined the RAF.

It had come about because, while I was at Oxford, I'd joined the University Air Squadron, the pleasure of flying being second to none, as far as I was concerned. When war was declared, it seemed a natural progression for me to volunteer for the RAF. For Pa this was a blow, and he found it hard to take. He didn't understand planes. For him war and soldiering was guns and barbed wire, bayonets and tanks. Getting to grips with the enemy. Although he didn't say it as such, I got the feeling from him that he felt "the flyboys" as he called them, were too cowardly to confront the enemy face to face. What with that, and his feeling that I'd betrayed him because I hadn't joined his old regiment as Edward had done, it made things difficult for us when we met. Not that things had been that easy before between Pa and myself, anyway. I don't know whether it was bitterness over being invalided out of the army after being wounded, or whether it was just he wasn't the kind of man who liked children much, even his sons. All I did know was, once Edward and I had stopped being infants, Pa had been difficult to make conversation with. There was something very reserved about him. And very angry. I wasn't looking forward to seeing him again and maybe getting into another argument with him. Still, I wasn't only going home to see him, I was going to see Ma and see how she was bearing up.

Our family home was near Regent's Park, in the centre of London, walking distance from everywhere, as Pa said. You could walk to the West End, you could walk in the park. It was one of those large old houses with bow windows at the front. Just like the Regiment had been handed down from father to son, so had the house. It was a family heirloom and would be handed on to Edward when Pa died, though Edward had always told me he didn't really want it. Edward wanted to live in the countryside where he could ride and shoot and fish. He once said the only things he could shoot from this house were the animals in Regent's Park Zoo.

When I arrived home I could see that Ma wasn't bearing up too well. Although she forced a smile and gave me a hug when she saw me, I could see that she'd just been crying.

"What on earth's the matter?" I asked her.

"It's Edward," said my father behind her as he came into the hall from his study.

"Edward?" I asked, puzzled. Then I laughed and gave Ma a hug. "If you're worried because you haven't heard from him, don't be. I had a letter from him only yesterday. He's fine, but he did say he wondered if you'd got his letters."

"We've heard," said my mother. She moved away from me and went to the hall table. She picked up a telegram and gave it to me.

"This arrived this morning," she said.

The words were very stark and simple. "Regret to inform your son Edward Smith missing in action."

I put the telegram back on the hall table. I didn't know what to say. Edward, missing in action. That usually only meant one thing: *dead, but we're afraid we can't find his body*. I felt numb, a cold sort of anger. Edward, so full of life, always joking, always the life and soul of any party, lying dead out there somewhere presumably in the snows of Norway.

I put my arm around Ma and forced a smile.

"All that means is he's missing," I said, trying to cheer her up. "He could have been taken prisoner and the other side are taking their time about letting us know. Or he might have escaped, be hiding out somewhere, unable to get in touch." I forced another smile. Like the first, it was one I didn't really feel. "Edward'll be all right, I'm sure of it. Look at the scrapes he used to get into when we were boys, but he always came up smiling. He'll turn up safe and sound, you'll see!"

But my words sounded hollow even to me.

The rest of that day was dismal. Ma tried to be cheerful for my sake, chatting about what the neighbours were up to, who was joining up in which regiment, who was getting married to who. Pa didn't say much. He never said much at the best of times; now with Edward gone missing like this, he was even more quiet than usual.

At least it meant he didn't start criticizing me or the RAF, so we never got into a row. However, I was glad when it came time for me to return to Hornchurch.

The streets of London were in darkness as I headed back to base. Blackout time: all the windows covered; all vehicles with their headlights hooded. With my brother missing, presumed dead, and the Germans just twenty miles away across the Channel, poised to invade, it was a dark time in more ways than one.

Dogfight After Dogfight

I got back to my squadron and was presented with my new Spitfire by Crusty with the warning words: "Take good care of this one."

Early the next morning I sat out in the warm sunshine with the rest of 327 Squadron and 58 Squadron and waited to be sent up. We sat around in deckchairs, on wooden crates, on anything we could find to sit comfortably. Tug Banks had even discovered an old armchair from somewhere and had dumped it outside the Operations Hut. He now reclined on it in comfort and luxury. I made do with one of the old wooden deckchairs. All of us wore our flying gear, complete with helmets, ready and waiting. When the call came there was no time to waste getting ready, it was run to the plane and get airborne as fast as possible.

"Maybe they won't come today," murmured Dob, who was sitting next to me on an old battered wooden armchair. "Not after what we did to them yesterday."

"Oh?" I asked, intrigued. "What happened yesterday?"

"Well, young Bonzo," grinned Tug, "while you were enjoying the delights of London, some of us were heavily engaged in trying to defeat the enemy."

I hadn't told them about Edward going missing, so Dob and Tug just assumed I'd spent the day relaxing with my parents. And although they knew from things I'd said that my father disapproved of my going into the RAF, I hadn't let on how deep his hurt and anger went, so there was no way for them to know that my day's leave hadn't been a day of enjoyment but one of sadness and misery.

"Yesterday was a triumph of co-operation," put in Dob. "11 Group and 10 Group working together with pretty spectacular results."

Here at Hornchurch we were part of Fighter Command's 11 Group, which covered the south-east of England. 10 Group was the Fighter Command Group to the west of us, covering Somerset, Devon and Dorset and the western counties.

Apparently radar had picked up a large number of German planes coming in to attack a shipping convoy.

"Reports say that only four of the ships made it to port out of the original convoy of twenty," grunted Tug. "Sixteen ships lost. But the Jerries paid dearly for it. We hit them hard. By the end of it we reckon they'd lost sixty planes to our nineteen. It might make them have second thoughts about attacking again today."

As if to prove him wrong, at that moment the siren sounded. Immediately we all leapt out of our chairs and began to run towards our planes. Over the loudspeaker came the voice of the flight controller instructing us: "327 Squadron take off and patrol base. Further information in the air."

I climbed on to the wing and clambered into the cockpit of my Spitfire. Starting my engine, I began my run over the grass, using the brakes and throttle to swing the plane from side to side. The Spitfire's long nose made forward vision almost impossible. It was wonderful in the air but on the ground the machine was difficult to handle, and as a result more than one pilot had crashed his plane even before take-off.

I aimed the Spitfire at the boundary of the airfield, turning her nose gently into the wind, and opened up the throttle to four pounds of boost. The Spitfire had great acceleration. I pushed the stick forward to lift the tail and get a good airflow over the elevators, and became airborne almost at once, soaring into the sky, my wheels up.

Pulling the control back, I set the throttle to get a good climbing speed of 200 miles an hour. Now, safely airborne, I slid the perspex hood of the cockpit shut.

Dob and I then slotted ourselves into our V-formation, to one side and just behind of Tug's leading plane: Dob to his right as Green 2, and me to Tug's left as Green 3.

We reached 15,000 feet and then levelled out. As we flew,

every plane in the formation – the whole squadron – weaved from side to side. That way it was easier to see the enemy if they were approaching. And if one of us spotted anything we alerted all the others at once.

Over the radio came the voice of the controller, saying: "Hello, Red Leader." Our Squadron Leader, Jerry Payne, was Red Leader, right at the front. As always, Blue and Green Sections were just behind.

"Reading you, Control," came Payne's voice.

"Bandits at 25,000 feet, coming at you on a direct interception course."

"Read that, Control," responded Payne. "OK, chaps," he said to us. "All sections up to 28,000 feet. Let's hit them from above and give them a surprise."

This time the German air fleet was a mixture of Dornier bombers, Junkers JU87s (Stuka dive-bombers), and Messerschmitt 109s. As always the 109s were riding shotgun for the bombers. After all, the aim of the German raids was to bomb Britain into submission, so the bombers were our main targets, not the fighters. But to get to the Dorniers we had to get past the 109s.

Battle started at once. Red Section swooped down into the attack, Blue following, and our Green Section behind them. Within seconds the air was a mass of fighter planes soaring, wheeling and leaving white trails of criss-crossed smoke. The large Dorniers kept in their steady paths while we flew at them, hitting them when and where we could. The Stukas were more manoeuvrable than the Dorniers and some took evasive action.

While Tug engaged the 109 fighter escorts in a dogfight, Dob and I went for the nearest Dornier. He let it have a burst of tracer into its nose, while I went for its tailplane. Without a tail any plane was as good as dead.

My burst smashed into the Dornier's rear, blowing away its rudder and ripping holes in the rear elevators. The bomber lurched in the sky, and then Dob came round again and let off another burst into its rear end that finished it off. The Dornier began to plunge earthwards, and as we watched we saw the crew leap out one after the other, their parachutes opening and billowing out white.

But there was no time to admire our handiwork on the Dornier because now we were under attack from more 109s as they came in to protect their other bombers.

The aerial battle went on for about twenty minutes, although it seemed much longer. The surviving Dorniers dropped their bomb loads and then turned to head for the coast, and the Channel. The Stukas did the same. I got one of the Stukas as it came back up after its bombing run, my tracer of bullets raking completely along its side. I felt a sense of satisfaction as black smoke billowed out from its engine.

It went into a dive. I knew it wouldn't be coming back up. That was one Stuka that wouldn't be dive-bombing again.

As the surviving bombers and fighter planes headed out to sea, we gave chase, but not too far.

"Back to base, Squadron," came Red Leader's voice over my radio as we flew out over the sea. "Save some fuel for next time."

He was right, of course. More than one over-keen pilot had given chase to retreating enemy planes, and then found himself over the English Channel with the red light winking to tell him he was out of fuel. Ditching in the sea wasn't an experience I fancied. Planes tended to sink very fast once they hit the water. And the chances of being picked up by British boats became that much slimmer the further you were from the English coast.

I turned my plane and followed the rest of the squadron back across the Kent countryside, and then dropped down as we approached Essex and our base.

We came in to land and taxied over towards the Control Hut. As we did I counted the planes. Twelve of us had gone up. Ten had come back. I hoped our two missing pilots had had the same luck that I'd had: that they'd been able to bail out and were even now maybe sitting somewhere safe, eating bacon and eggs and drinking tea in some friendly farmer's kitchen.

As we walked over to the mess hall I joined up with Dob Masters.

"Any idea who didn't make it back?" I asked.

"I saw Proctor bail out early on," said Dob. "I'm pretty sure he's safe. I'm not so sure about Squires."

Walter Squires was a very courageous fighter pilot with Red Section. He had taught me a lot when I first joined the squadron. Defence was his strong point. "Always look for a way out before you go in," was his motto. It looked as if this time he hadn't been lucky enough to find a way out.

We had barely been in the mess hall for ten minutes, drinking a welcome cup of tea, when the siren to scramble us went again.

"Not again!" said Tug. "Don't those Germans have anything better to do?!"

It went on like this for the next ten days. It was the heaviest concentration of attacks we'd experienced so far. Six or seven times a day the siren sounded to send us up, and into the air we went, fighting dogfight after dogfight, shooting their planes down, watching them shoot our planes down. Still they kept coming. Early in the morning. Late at night. Throughout the day. Attack after attack. And it seemed as if each time we came back there was one or two of us missing. Familiar faces no longer there, to be replaced by fresh-faced youngsters straight out of training. But there weren't enough pilots left in training to fill the gaps that were appearing. It was the same at every air base across England. New squadrons were made up. Polish pilots. Czech. Canadians. New Zealanders. Different accents, different languages, the same aim: defend England.

It seemed like there was never a minute when we weren't either up there fighting them, or waiting for the Germans to attack. Sleep at night was out of the question as we waited for the scramble siren to go off. After a week of this some of the lads were so tired that they didn't even bother to get out of their planes when we landed, just taxied to a space on the field, switched off the engine, and then fell asleep in their cockpits.

On the tenth morning, 14 August, I woke up after about an hour's sleep – although it only seemed like a few minutes – as dawn was breaking. The sky was clear. Quiet.

I stepped outside the hut and stood looking out over the airfield and thinking how quiet it was, how very English, the red sun coming up through the trees that bordered the eastern side of the airfield. It was a perfect August morning. Dob Masters joined me.

"Jerry's late today," he said.

"Their alarm clocks can't have gone off," I joked.

We wandered over to our chairs set out on the grass and sat down to admire the morning.

"Maybe they've given up?" said Dob.

"Ssssh!" I grinned. "You said that before, and look what happened!"

"Yes, but they can't have that many planes left after the last three days," Dob pointed out. "We must have shot down hundreds of them. Not just us but all over."

"We've lost planes too," I pointed out. "In fact, sometimes I think that the winner of this will be the side that has the last plane left flying."

We sat there, watching the sun slowly rise, and heard the birds singing their song in the trees to the rising sun.

"At least we've got radar," sighed Dob.

I nodded. There was no doubt that it was our radar that had given us the edge in this battle so far. The whole of the south coast and parts of the east coast of England were dotted with radar stations. They could give us good advance warning of an attack. The Germans had tried to bomb the radar stations, but luckily so far they'd had little effect. Some of the tall radar masts had been bombed to the ground and some of the receiver huts had been damaged, but because of the large number of radar stations strung out across the defence line the radar warning system had kept going. At least, that was what I believed at that time on that August morning, sitting there in the warm early-morning sun with Dob Masters.

The siren sounded. Scramble. With the radar system as our first defence we would have about five minutes to get to our planes and off the ground, time enough to be there on an intercept course. Only today we didn't have five minutes. We didn't have five seconds. As Dob and I got up, we heard them: the drones of the engines of heavy German bombers. Then we saw them, at the same time as we heard the controller's voice over the loudspeaker order: "Enemy bombing formation approaching! Take cover immediately!"

"They must have knocked out our radar!" gasped Dob.

As we looked up the first bomb came screaming directly towards us.

Bombed!

"Down!" I yelled, and I threw myself at Dob. We both crashed to the ground as the bomb whistled over our heads. Seconds later it exploded only about 200 yards away. A shower of rocks and earth cascaded down on us.

I rolled over on the ground and looked behind me. A huge smouldering crater had been blown into the ground. Dob and I looked up as we heard the Stukas coming back.

"The shelter!" I shouted, and we both ran for the nearest bomb shelter. As we did so we heard the nearest bomber's machine guns open fire and bullets began to rip into the ground behind us. I threw myself the last few yards in through the entrance of the bomb shelter and rolled down the concrete steps into the shelter itself. Dob fell down the steps, landing on top of me.

Six other people were already inside it: two pilots and four ground crew. Dob and I picked ourselves up from the hard floor and shook dirt and cement off our clothes. Smoke and dust billowed down into the shelter as the bombs dropped on the base. With each fresh explosion the building seemed to rise out of the ground, and then settle back down.

The Germans must have knocked out some of our radar positions to be able to get this far without us being given any warning. With the radar gone that left only the physical observation posts dotted around, and by the time they could get a warning to the air bases the enemy was on target, as we had just found out to our cost. I wondered what the damage was like outside. How many planes had the German bombers destroyed? What shape was the airfield in?

The bombing raid seemed to go on for ever, though it must have only lasted for about five minutes. When at last we heard the sound of the All Clear we emerged from the shelter.

The airfield was a mess. Three Spitfires had been completely destroyed. Another two planes had been badly shot up, with gaping holes in the cockpit hoods and fuselage, as well as loose-hanging wings. One of the buildings had taken a direct hit and was now just a smouldering pile of bricks and rubble. One of the runways had two deep craters in it. Fortunately the other runways had only suffered minor damage.

Dob and I wandered out across the airfield, inspecting the aftermath of the attack. We knew that other airfields had been badly bombed, but it was the first time either of us had experienced it first hand here at Hornchurch.

"What a mess!" groaned Dob.

"Attention!" came the flight controller's voice over the loudspeaker. "Station commander's orders: every available man and woman to report to Operations and collect a shovel or other tools. All holes to be filled in as priority."

Dob and I hurried along with everyone else, pilots, canteen staff, radio operators, clerks, to collect our tools. We were lucky the Germans didn't return for a further attack. It was my guess that they thought they'd put Hornchurch out of action for a good while so they were turning their attacks to the other bases. Luckily they'd underestimated the determination of everybody on the air base to get Hornchurch active again.

For the next few hours we slaved away, muscles aching as we shovelled earth into wheelbarrows and dumped it back into the craters, gradually filling them up. After two hours of this, those of us who weren't used to so much physical labour were ready to take to our beds and get some rest, but we knew that time was short. We had to get the base back into operation. No runways meant no planes in the air.

By the end of the afternoon every hole was repaired, with the exception of the main runway with its two giant craters. That would take a little longer. The main thing was that the airfield was operational again.

We'd just finished filling in the holes and were looking

forward to going to the mess and giving our tired limbs a rest, when the siren sounded.

"Scramble!" came the flight controller's voice. "Bandits coming in from the east!"

"Already!" groaned Dob.

And so it began again.

As it turned out our radar system hadn't been knocked out completely, just a few of the masts. By extending the range of the existing radar while they were repaired, our coastal early-warning system was soon functional again.

We flew another sortie that evening just to show the Germans that they hadn't put us out of the picture, and between us our squadron bagged two German bombers and two fighters for the loss of just one of our planes.

The next day, 15 August, brought the biggest German attack so far. It was as if, just when we thought it couldn't get any worse, it did.

Time and time again we went up into the air as wave after wave of German bombers and fighters poured into the attack. By dusk at the end of the day we were all at the point of exhaustion. When you get that tired your concentration starts to go, and when you're flying a machine at 350 miles an hour against crack opposition who are determined to kill you, you need every ounce of your concentration if you are to survive.

Maybe it was the exhaustion, maybe the feeling that he'd been in dogfights so many times and that he was starting to become invincible, whatever it was, it was towards the evening that Dob Masters was shot down. He and I were coming in to attack a Heinkel bomber and the Heinkel's machine-gunner hit Dob's plane with a tracer that tore off his propeller. I didn't know if the bullets had hit Dob himself, all I saw in that split second was Dob's plane go into an abrupt dive, spinning as it dropped, nose-first, wings whirling round like a windmill. In situations like this there is a danger of the pilot "redding out". This can happen when a pilot changes direction too quickly or goes into a sudden dive, pushing blood up into his brain. All you can see is red. Apart from that you are blind. I just hoped Dob had had time to bail out before that happened.

I was determined to pay the Heinkel back for hitting Dob. I came at the bomber from the front and placed a tracer of bullets into its nose and carried it on right along the length of the plane. Then I flew up, did a turn and a loop, and came back for my second run at it. That was my mistake. I should have remembered Walter Squires's advice: "Always look for a way out." Instead, I was so determined to down the Heinkel that I didn't see the Messerschmitt coming at me from behind. The first I knew about it was an enormous thump from my port side that seemed to knock my plane sideways, and then I was dropping out of the sky.

I managed to bring the Spitfire under control and levelled out, and then tried to climb back up again, only it wouldn't respond. It was then I looked out at my port wing and realized that it had been badly hit; there were gaping holes in the wing fuselage. I could even see parts of the Browning machine guns in the wing, buckled and bent. Without proper weapons and with only one good wing, I was going to have to do my best to get back to base before she gave up the ghost and I crashed.

I turned and set a course for base. The plane was rocking and bucking like a mad horse, trying to fly to one side. I had to hold on like grim death to the joystick to stop it from turning in a complete circle and then going into a dive. It carried on like this every bit of the way as I limped back to Essex. I did think of looking for a nearer airfield, but I was determined to keep that rash promise I'd made to Crusty Pearson; I wasn't going to give him the pleasure of reprimanding me for losing any more planes. I'd bring this one back even if both of us were in bits.

The nearer I got to base, the harder it was to keep the Spitfire in the air. In the end I just prayed that there was enough wind to help me get home.

I could now see the green grass and the airstrips of

Hornchurch just ahead. Judging my approach, I brought the crippled plane in on as straight a line as I could, but the wind that had brought me so far home was now my enemy as I changed direction to try to bring the Spitfire in to land. I revved the engine just enough to give me the speed I needed to fight against the wind, and then I was wobbling in towards the ground, the plane going all over the place as it came in.

I hit the ground with a thud, bounced, and then came down again, and immediately the plane tried to go into a circular motion on the ground. I managed to pull it up just short of the Control Building. Crusty Pearson was hurrying towards me from Control as I stepped down from my bullet-strafed cockpit.

"There you are, Flight," I said, gesturing at the ruined wing. "I said I'd bring the next one back."

I then waited for the rest of the squadron to return, and hoped there'd be news of Dob. There wasn't. The squadron came home. Dob didn't.

The New Pilot

Dob's replacement arrived two days later. Gordon McBurn, a 19-year-old New Zealander. He was a bit shorter than me, about five feet eight, with a mass of ginger hair. He'd been in England for the past two months in training, having come over to "do my bit for the old country", as he called it. His family had originally gone to New Zealand from Scotland just before he was born. With a name like McBurn, it seemed natural that we nicknamed him Scotty.

I now moved up to Green 2, taking Dob's place as first wingman to our Section Leader, while Scotty took over from me as Green 3.

That first morning when Scotty joined our squadron, Tug Banks left me to look after him and fill him in on how things worked, while he made some adjustments to his plane. Luckily for us the Germans were late that morning; some fog over the Channel had given us a well-needed respite for a few hours.

I learnt that Scotty had joined the RNZAF when he was eighteen and a half, the youngest age at which he could join up.

"The way a lot of us in New Zealand see it," said Ginger,

"is that if Britain falls, then all of us out in New Zealand are just going to end up as part of the German Reich. It won't be long before we have German troops jackbooting through Christchurch and Wellington, and there's no way we're going to let that happen if we can help it."

He told me there were about a hundred New Zealanders just like him who'd come out to fly with the RAF and defend the country that was the hub of the Empire. Scotty's training in New Zealand had mainly been on Tiger Moths. The first time he'd been in a Spitfire had been just six weeks ago, two weeks after he'd begun his training at Kenley. Now here he was, about to go into battle against hardened and experienced German fighter pilots. As I looked at him, sitting out on the airfield in his flying gear, I reflected that – even though we were the same age – he seemed so much younger than me. I'd been up there, dealing out death and narrowly escaping it. I'd seen my comrades die. I'd shot and killed other human beings. As I looked at him I felt a sudden wave of sadness.

So often it was the newest pilots who died, often during their first air battle. They didn't have the experience of fighting in the sky, that almost sixth sense that comes with being in dogfight after dogfight, that heightened sensation when you know that someone is on your tail, or has you in their gunsights, and you abruptly change course. If a new pilot could survive their first encounter with the enemy then he had a chance of surviving the next. I decided to pass on some tips to Scotty that I'd picked up in the hope that they kept him alive, at least during his first encounter.

"When we first go up, do exactly what Tug Banks says," I told him. "He's our section leader and he's survived longer than any of us. Trust him. If he says fly head-on at them, then fly head-on at them. He knows what he's doing.

"The next thing to remember is, when you're up there on your own, forget all the fancy stuff. That going into a tight spin or looping the perfect loop and all that clever stuff. It's OK in a flying circus, but it also fixes your line of flight for the opposition, and the more time they've got to get a good fix on your flight path, the easier it is for them to shoot you down. Keep them guessing about the direction you're going next.

"Come at them out of the sun if it's possible. That'll blind them. And watch out for them trying to turn you into the sun. They'll do it if they can.

"Remember, our job is to hit the bombers. If we knock one of their fighters down then it's a bonus, but it's the bombers doing the damage to our airfields and cities. When you attack a bomber, aim for the cockpit. Knock out the pilot and the plane goes down. That means hitting it from the front. The only trouble with that is the machine-gunner in their cockpit will have you as a direct target. Another way is to hit the bomber's tailplane, but you have to hit it very hard, blow it away, and those German bombers are pretty well made.

"I've found the best and safest way is to hit a plane directly from behind. If you're lucky, the tailplane hides you from view as you come in.

"When you're shooting, remember always to fire ahead of the enemy plane. You've got to allow for their speed. Fire just before they get into your gunsights. Unless you're coming at them dead ahead or from dead behind, of course.

"In battle, try to avoid shadowing any of your own wingmen too closely. Two planes flying together in close formation are an easier target to hit than two planes flying erratically all over the sky, and often it's the second plane that gets it because the enemy has used the first plane as a marker.

"Remember that the enemy is no different to you. He's as scared as you. His plane is no better than yours. And in the case of the German fighter pilots, he has to remain with his bombers. He's not supposed to fly all over the sky, he has to stay there, which makes him a better target. And don't take chances. Before you go in, look for the way out."

As I said these last words, I reflected that this was the same advice that Walter Squires had given to me.

We didn't have time to think about this for long, because just then the voice of control came over the speakers: "327 Squadron, Blue and Green Sections. Scramble."

The next second we were running for our planes. I gave Scotty a thumbs-up sign as he clambered into his Spitfire. Tug was already running towards his. We climbed in, helmets on, engines started up, parachutes and safety harnesses fastened, chocks away, and then we were off, across the grass, and up into the air.

The despatch of just one or two sections of a squadron had become standard practice of late with Fighter Command Group 11. Done on a rota basis, it gave the pilots a little more breathing space on the ground, and they could be scrambled if needed. They were also there in reserve if the enemy suddenly came with a second attack from another direction.

"Control to sections. Course 120 and climb to 15,000 feet," came the voice of the flight control over our headphones.

I set my compass to 120 degrees and followed Tug as we went into our climb. I looked across at Scotty in Green 3. He flew well, maintaining his position level parallel with mine, behind and just above Tug's plane.

The altimeter needle moved round the clock as we climbed up into clouds, and then we broke through to find ourselves in clear sky above them.

Once again we heard the voice of control through our R-T: "Green Section. Control calling. Bandit approaching you from the east at 14,000 feet. Continue on present course. Over to you."

"Read that, Control," we heard Tug answer. "OK, chaps, tally-ho."

Scotty and I followed Tug in a straight line, skimming the tops of the clouds, keeping our eyes peeled for the approaching German planes. According to control they should be 1000 feet below us, within the belt of cloud.

"Down we go, chaps," came Tug's voice.

We followed him as he made a shallow dive into the thick cloud. Somewhere within it were our enemy, but whether they were ahead or behind us, we couldn't tell. I guessed that Tug was flying on instinct and luck, which made up the pilot's sixth sense. They were here somewhere, but where?

Suddenly, whether because the wind had shifted the clouds or because there was a break in them, we were back in clear sky, and heading straight towards two Dorniers flying in line astern formation, with their Me109 escorts.

"Fire!" yelled Tug.

We all three pressed our fire switches at once. We must have caught them by surprise as we came so suddenly out of the cloud at them. Our bullets smashed into the front of the first Dornier and we barely had time to register that it was on its way down with thick black smoke pouring from its shattered front, before we were almost on the second one. The Me109s moved to defend their bomber.

Tug and I took out the leading Me109s, pouring bullets

into them as they came for us, although firing from one of the Messerschmitts tore through my cockpit just above my head. Then we soared away.

Out of the corner of my eye I saw that Scotty was still with us, keeping close to us, as I'd told him to. I hope he also remembered my bit of advice about separating once the dogfight really got under way, otherwise he could find himself in real trouble.

Tug swooped down towards the surviving Dornier, and as he did so the machine-gunner at the top of the bomber opened fire, forcing Tug to swing away.

I saw the Dornier's bomb load leave the belly of the plane, long sticks in a falling line. I managed to get off a burst from my machine guns, but the Dornier turned in an arc and my tracer went harmlessly past its nose.

The Me109s were also beginning their turn and heading back. They weren't scared off; they were just low on fuel.

We gave chase for a few moments, just long enough to make sure they were definitely leaving, then Tug said: "OK, chaps, home. Don't waste fuel and bullets. They'll be needed for next time."

The three of us turned and began our return flight to Hornchurch, still keeping alert in case one of the Me109s should change its mind and decide to attack us from the rear. One Dornier and two Messerschmitts down for no loss to our side. Even Flight Sergeant Crusty Pearson should be satisfied with that.

We touched down on the grass one after the other: Tug first, then me, then Scotty.

Tug and I caught up with Scotty as he clambered down from the cockpit of his plane. He took his helmet and goggles off, and the expression on his face looked shaken, but at the same time exhilarated.

"Well done, young 'un," Tug said to him. "Keep flying like that and we might have a section that stays together. I'll see you both in the Mess."

Scotty smiled as Tug walked off to the Control Dispersal Hut to report in.

"I don't think I've ever been so scared as just before we went in for that first attack," he said.

"It was the same for all of us," I said. "It's one thing flying for fun, it's entirely another when someone up there is trying to kill you."

"But once it started I didn't feel scared any more," he said. "Even though it got worse, bullets flying around."

"I know," I said. "It's strange. It's like some animal instinct for survival takes over. You don't think, you just act."

I patted him on the shoulder.

"Well done, Scotty. You're one of us now."

The Blitz Begins

The war in the air over Britain continued that way for the next three weeks. During that time we went up, we fought, we came back. We lost more pilots and planes. Scotty grew in confidence each time he went up, even bagging five kills himself during those three weeks.

I had two letters from Ma during that time, saying she was worried about me, and also that there was still no firm news of Edward, although the War Office had written saying that "after this length of time it is regretted that it must be considered that Lieutenant Edward Smith has been killed in action, the whereabouts of his body unknown". Ma, however, still clung to the fact that as Edward's body hadn't been found it meant that he was still alive somewhere, maybe in a German hospital or Prisoner-of-War camp.

"Your pa says we have to accept the worst," she wrote. "He says we have to admit to ourselves that Edward is dead, but I find it so hard. I really will not believe it until I see Edward's body for myself."

Meanwhile, we fought on. The Luftwaffe continued their campaign to try and destroy our airfields. Just as many times they were successful, destroying our planes on the ground and our runways. But many times they paid dearly for that success as we shot down their bombers and their fighters. However, as more and more of our planes and pilots never returned, I couldn't help wondering sometimes if we could keep taking losses at this rate. The Germans just kept on coming back in even larger numbers; it felt like we were fighting an uphill battle.

Then, on the night of 7 September, Scotty and I were sitting in the mess with most of the rest of the squadron, having a drink, when Tug came in with a face like thunder.

"The Jerries are bombing London," he said.

We all hurried out of the mess and stood there on the airfield, looking towards the south. Even from this distance we could see the black sky above London glowing a dull red and hear the distant CRUMP CRUMP CRUMP as wave after wave of bombs fell on the capital.

All we could do was stand there, wishing we could go up against the bombers, but there was nothing we could do because we risked getting shot down by our own anti-aircraft guns.

The anti-aircraft guns sited around London were the first line of defence against night air attacks. When they were blazing away sending tracers into the night sky, they couldn't distinguish between a German plane and a British one.

We hardly slept that night. Next morning, as Scotty and I waited to go up, Tug told us the terrible news about the previous night's attack.

"I heard about it from my cousin in the War Office," he said. "The Germans bombed the whole of the East End of London right up to five o'clock this morning. Four hundred and thirty civilians killed, with over 1,600 seriously injured."

It was a tragic blow.

Later that morning, 8 September, as we flew over the East End of London, we saw the signs of the devastation caused during the night. It was sickening. I'd seen the results of bombs before, but mainly the damage to our own airfields. Below me whole streets had disappeared. Buildings flattened into rubble. Parts of the East End of London were still burning, a thick pall of smoke rising. Ships were smashed and broken at their moorings in the docks. The dockyards themselves were burning. Acrid smoke drifted up into the sky from the wreckage of the warehouses as the stored timber, paint and chemicals smouldered, every now and then bursting into flame.

The Germans didn't come that morning, but they came again that afternoon: a huge wave of bombers flying in formation with their fighter escorts. We guessed that daytime bombing would afford them greater accuracy for hitting their targets. Or maybe they preferred to take their chances against the RAF rather than the anti-aircraft guns. Or maybe they were stepping up their bombing of London in preparation for the invasion, which everyone had said could come any day now.

Whatever the reason, the German air fleet came and it bombed London. We harassed them as best we could on that first afternoon of daylight bombing of the capital, and they certainly went back with fewer planes than set out, but there was no mistaking that London suffered badly.

That night the Germans returned for a second night raid, and once more we could only stay at our base and look to the south and watch helplessly as London was bombed and burned. I thought of Ma and Pa in their house, and wondered how they were. Were they safe? Had our house in Regent's Park been touched?

The pattern went on like this for the next three days: the German heavy bombers attacking London during the night, and then coming back again during the day, usually in the afternoon, when we would swoop up and meet them, each time flying further south and east to try and intercept them before they actually got to London.

The only good thing about it, from our point of view, was that the Germans' concentration on bombing London kept them away from our airfields and gave us a chance. We'd lost a lot of planes so far on the ground to German attacks on our airfields.

As the daylight bombing raids increased we flew more and more sorties, with more and more of our planes in the air at any one time. Soon we seemed to be spending all our time in our cockpits. It hardly seemed to be worth getting out when you knew you'd just have to clamber back in again minutes later, buckle up, and take off again.

It was impossible to grab much sleep at night because of the bombing raids on London. Just being a few miles north-east of the capital, we were constantly on the alert in case we were bombed ourselves.

So it went on. Barely any sleep at night. None during the day. And flying sortie after sortie against the enemy.

The strain and exhaustion began to take its toll on all of us. A leave rota was worked out giving us all a chance to get away from the base for twenty-four hours and unwind. Some of the chaps went away for their day and simply slept. Others did the exact opposite, went to the parts of London that weren't being bombed, the West End, and did the round of restaurants and nightclubs, and came back even more tired than when they went.

When 11 September arrived, it was 327's Green Section's time for leave. Tug Banks went north, heading homeward to see his wife. Scotty and I grabbed a lift with a pilot from 58 Squadron, Freddy Fox. Freddy was heading for London to sample the nightclubs.

"If I'm going to die tomorrow, then at least I'll die with a smile on my face from the happy memories," Freddy chuckled as he drove.

I sat beside him in the front seat and wondered what I'd find when I got back to Regent's Park. I wondered if there would be any word about Edward. Maybe by some miracle he would have turned up, though this didn't seem the time when miracles happened much.

Scotty was going to visit some relatives of his who lived in Barnet, just north of London, so we dropped him off at their house first, and then continued on into London. We drove down the A1. The nearer we got to the centre of London, the greater were the signs of bomb-damage.

Many roads had been closed off. In some cases the wardens were worried that the bomb-damaged houses alongside the roads would suddenly fall down and kill someone. In other cases the road surface had simply vanished and been replaced by great craters many feet deep.

Freddy dropped me off a few streets away from where my parents lived. It was as near as he could get.

"See you back at Hornchurch, old chum!" he grinned cheerily before driving off.

I picked my way over rubble and around craters. Some of the crushed buildings were still smouldering – obviously they had been attacked on the previous night's air raid. I turned the corner into Ranalegh Place, and stopped, my heart suddenly going into shock. There, where our house should have been, was just a pile of rubble.

Bitter Words At Home

"John!" called a woman's voice.

I turned and saw one of our neighbours, Mrs Danvers, hurrying towards me.

Mrs Danvers was a tall, thin lady of about fifty. When I had been a small boy she'd always appeared to be ancient, mainly because of the old-fashioned way she dressed: lace collars and long skirts. As I grew older, Mrs Danvers never seemed to age. She'd always been kind to me and Edward, always finding sweets for both of us. Nothing had ever seemed to disturb her, but now she looked deeply upset.

"I thought it was you," she said. "Terrible, isn't it? We were hit last night. Well, not us particularly, but the street."

"Ma and Pa…?" I asked, gesturing at the ruins of our house.

"They've gone to your Aunt Louise's," said Mrs Danvers.

"Both of them?" I asked.

It was a stupid question but I was still in a sort of daze. At the sight of that rubble I found it hard to believe that they'd survived.

"Yes," she said. "Luckily for them they were in the Anderson shelter next door at Mr Page's. They'd gone there because they thought he was frightened on his own and needed company."

Some people had made their Anderson shelters quite comfortable. Mr Page, our next-door neighbour, was one of them. He'd even got a couple of armchairs and a table inside it, with an oil lamp so he could sit and read.

I thanked Mrs Danvers for her news and then hurried off to my Aunt Louise's.

Aunt Louise was my mother's elder sister. She had a small flat in Gloucester Place, about a mile away from my parents' house. I could imagine that having to stay with Aunt Louise would only make Pa more irritable than ever. He was used to living in a large house and having his own things around him. To have to live in three tiny rooms with someone else, even if it was his sister-in-law, would certainly put him in a bad temper.

Pa was out when I arrived at Aunt Louise's, just Ma and Aunt Louise were sitting having tea.

"John!" said Mum, her face lighting up as she saw me. She gave me a big hug, and then she got all flustered as she looked round the tiny flat.

"You might have told us you were coming," she reprimanded me. "We could have made arrangements for where you can stay tonight."

"Sorry, Ma," I said. "It was all short notice."

"Leave the boy alone, Amanda," put in Aunt Louise. "Putting him up here is no problem. He can sleep in the hallway, if he doesn't mind draughts. I can put a rug and some blankets down for him there."

"Sleeping in the hallway will be perfect, Aunt Louise," I said. "It'll be a lot more comfortable than sleeping in the cockpit of a Spitfire, which is what I seem to have been doing most of lately."

Aunt Louise poured me out a cup of tea and found me some sweet biscuits, which I wolfed down. Sweet biscuits were becoming a rarity in wartime Britain, as were many other things, such as chocolates. German attacks on the merchant convoys had all but stopped the import of raw sugar into the country.

We were sitting chatting, mainly Ma telling me about the house being bombed, when Pa arrived, back from his walk. He grunted and just nodded when he saw me. Aunt Louise went off to get another cup for him.

"The city is in a mess," he grunted. "Bombed buildings. Roads ruined." He looked at me accusingly. "I thought your lot were supposed to be protecting us?"

"We're doing what we can," I countered. "The Germans have got more planes than we've got. More pilots. And although we can go up against them in the daytime, it's out of the question at night. The anti-aircraft gunners can't distinguish between our planes and theirs. I don't know why you don't all go out to the country," I added. "Uncle Stephen's got a big enough house down in Wiltshire. You could all go and stay with him while this is going on."

"That's what I suggested," said Ma, "I told him my brother would be happy to have us, but your pa absolutely refuses."

"Of course I refuse!" snapped Pa. "If the King and Queen won't let themselves be driven out of Buckingham Palace by this upstart Austrian corporal, then I'm damned if I'm going to run away."

"It's not running away," I said. "It's just common sense."

"We're not going, and that's that," said Pa.

There was a heavy brooding silence for a few moments. Pa sat deep in thought, I stared out of the window, and Ma and Aunt Louise sat in an uncomfortable silence, not wanting to upset my father. Then Pa suddenly looked at me and snapped: "Of course, if you flyboys had done your job properly at Dunkirk we wouldn't be in this mess."

I stared at him, stunned.

"What do you mean?!" I demanded.

"Boys, boys," said Ma in soothing tones. "This is not the time to argue."

"I'm not arguing," said Pa stiffly, "I'm just stating facts. The RAF didn't give proper cover to our troops on the ground at Dunkirk. If they had, our troops would have been able to fight back and the Germans wouldn't be across the Channel right now, ready to invade."

This was just too much for me. Despite Ma's appealing look at me, I responded angrily.

"That's just not true!" I said. "The RAF gave as much support as they could. The RAF bombed German artillery positions and kept the Luftwaffe at bay. If it hadn't been for the RAF the losses at Dunkirk would have been even greater than they were!"

"Of course you'd say that, you're one of them!" snapped back my father. "You flyboys have no idea of what real fighting is like. Bombs dropping around you. Trenches. Men drowning in mud. Hand-to-hand fighting. You lot just fly around the sky popping at each other from a safe distance."

I could feel myself getting so angry. Thinking of Dob Masters, shot down and dead, and so many more of them who all died while serving their country and saving the lives of people like my father.

"Please, you two," pleaded my mother. "This isn't our house. Let's have no arguments."

For my mother's sake I held myself back. Pa, too, decided he'd said enough and he just sat there, staring into his teacup, an angry look on his face. I knew that he was angry at himself, for the wound in his leg which kept him out of active service in this war, but it didn't make me feel any better towards him.

The rest of the time passed in an awkward silence, with Ma and Aunt Louise making small talk, and Pa and I doing our best to avoid each other. That was difficult, though, in Aunt Louise's small flat with its three rooms. I was feeling that I couldn't stand the strain between myself and my father any more. I knew I'd have to go out somewhere, even if it was just for a walk. I didn't fancy spending the whole night cooped up here in Aunt Louise's flat with Pa. And then the air-raid sirens went off and let me know that I wouldn't have to. The German bombers were on their way. London was under attack.

Underground

The four of us hurried to the nearest shelter, in the underground station at Baker Street. The wail of the air-raid siren continued, a two-tone wail rising and falling, filling the air. Pa moved as fast as he could, but I could see that he was having difficulty because of his bad leg. I moved to help him, but he brushed me away with an angry: "Leave me alone! I'm not a complete invalid!"

Once again I bit my tongue and kept my silence, and turned my attention to Ma and Aunt Louise, but they were already walking along the street with speed, but without looking as if they were actually rushing. We were now in a whole procession of people, all heading for the Underground station. What struck me was how well-behaved most people were. As we got nearer I could see the steel-hatted figure of an air-raid warden, urging everyone, "No rushing, please! Keep it orderly!"

We reached the Underground station and hurried down the stationary escalators to the platforms below. There an astonishing sight met my eyes. I hadn't realized just how well the Londoners had adapted the Underground to meet the needs of bomb shelters.

Some families had even marked out their territory on the station platform with tables and chairs, and there were even a few beds that had somehow been manhandled down there.

There was a general atmosphere of good humour among the people, and recognition of each other as old friends.

We had barely reached the platform and found a place to sit, when the bombs began to fall. Even though we were so far underground, we could hear them explode, a mighty crash that made the walls of the Underground station shake and vibrate.

"Those are the big ones," explained Aunt Louise to me, almost as if she were giving a lesson to a small child. "We don't hear the smaller ones."

"Our warden says he thinks the incendiary bombs are the worst," added Ma. "They start a fire, and when there's a wind it can spread from building to building within seconds. Whole streets burnt out within minutes. And there's no escape."

I thought back to the time my plane had caught fire and I'd been able to bail out. No such possibility of escape for someone caught in a burning building.

"I don't know about that," said Aunt Louise thoughtfully. "Then there are these new ones they're dropping. The mine things. They're terrible."

"Landmines," said my father.

"Yes, those things," said Aunt Louise. "Honestly, John, they are absolutely huge. They drop them by parachute so that they don't go into the ground. That way, when they blow up, they do more damage. One of them came down in Marylebone Road but it didn't go off. I went to look at it. It must have been at least twelve feet long."

"Eight feet," corrected my father. "They're eight feet long."

"Well, they're certainly very big," said Aunt Louise. "As big as a small lorry."

I could only sit there and marvel at these two elderly – to me, at least – ladies sitting there and calmly discussing different sorts of bombs that were falling on them as if they were talking about new hats, or new dinner recipes.

The walls of the Underground station reverberated as more and more bombs dropped. Heavens knows what sort of devastation was going on outside. I felt sorry for the men and women of the civil-defence patrols and the fire brigades, out there in the middle of it, doing their best to put out the fires, and pull the dead and the wounded from the collapsed buildings.

Even down here in the underground I didn't feel safe. I expected the roof to come crashing down at any moment and all of us to be buried.

Suddenly, from a little distance along the platform, I heard the sound of a mouth organ strike up a tune. I recognized it as "Pennies From Heaven", which showed someone had a sense of humour because people started to sing the words:

"Every time it rains
It rains Pennies from Heaven."

And they laughed at the thought that the only thing raining down on us at the moment were thousands of tons of German bombs. After "Pennies From Heaven", someone started singing "Roll Out The Barrel". Then someone else joined in with another song, then another, and so on throughout the first few hours of that night underground: everyone singing as if it would drown out the constant noise of the bombs. Or, if it didn't drown it out, at least it would cheer everyone up and help them cope with it better. The small children and babies who'd started to cry with fright as the first bombs fell gradually quietened down as the community singing continued.

Eventually, despite the thuds and explosions of the bombs, people began to sleep, curled up or lying straight out on the platform. Soon the singing died away and underground London slept, with the rhythmic crashing of the constant bombing above them as a lullaby.

It was six o'clock the next morning before the all clear sounded, a steady two-minute blast on a siren. We came out of the depths of Baker Street Tube, bleary-eyed, and beheld a city devastated. Looking at the heaps of rubble, the torn and burning timbers, the broken glass, I could only marvel that we'd survived the night at all.

Pa went with Aunt Louise back to her flat, while I walked with Ma to the ruins of our house at Ranelagh Place. We were going to sort through the wreckage and see if we could find any of the family photographs that she was missing. In particular I knew she was looking for the one of Edward that had been in a silver frame on the sideboard in the sitting room.

As we walked, Ma tried to talk about Pa. She made excuses for him and the way he was with me: it was the pain in his leg, worry about Edward, etc. I let her talk, although I knew that deep down he had never forgiven me for not following him and Edward into the Fusiliers. Pa was stubborn, but so was I. I was sure it was my stubbornness that had kept me alive in my aerial battles.

Ma and I reached the wreckage of our old house and we began to sift through it, pulling off rafters, moving bricks.

Our next-door neighbour, Mr Page, saw what we were up to and came out to help. So did Mrs Danvers. Before I knew it, the rest of our street was helping me and Ma comb the wreckage.

We found lots of things: a canteen of silver cutlery that had been a wedding present to her from Pa's parents, pieces of china, all broken. And then I found it: the photo of Edward in its silver frame, the glass miraculously intact. I also found a photograph of the pair of us, Edward and me when we were small boys.

I gave them to Ma, and watched her wipe a tear from her eye and give a little smile.

"Finding that photo of Edward is an omen, Amanda," announced Mrs Danvers. "It's a sign telling you he's still alive."

"I know he is," said Ma quietly, looking at the photo. "Edward's out there somewhere. He'll come back to me, I know it."

I gave Ma a big hug.

"And wherever he is, he knows you're thinking of him," I said.

To be honest, I didn't know whether Edward was alive or dead. All I knew was that finding the photograph had made her happy, and for the moment that was all that mattered.

Mr Page came over and joined us. "If we find anything else, I'll keep it safe in the Anderson shelter for you until you come back," he told Ma.

We thanked him, and Mrs Danvers, and all the others. And then I walked Ma back to Aunt Louise's, her carrying the two photographs, me carrying the canteen of cutlery.

After that, there wasn't much left for me to do in London, so I headed back out towards Hornchurch, and back to battle.

Back into Action

Next morning I was back in my deckchair at the base, waiting to be scrambled into the air. Tug Banks came and sat himself down beside me and asked, "Everything all right, Bonzo?"

"Fine, skipper," I said.

"Only you looked a bit lost in thought. Everything go all right on leave?"

"Fine," I said. "Our house was bombed."

"Bad show," he sympathized. "Folks all right?"

I nodded. "They were sitting in next-door's shelter playing cards when it happened," I said. "They'll be fine."

"Good," he said. He looked reflectively up at the sky, in the direction we knew the German planes would come from. "My wife's feeling a bit under the weather with all this," he said. "She worries about me. I keep telling her I'll be fine, I'm like a cat with nine lives, but you know what wives can be like."

I nodded. I didn't, but it seemed the thing to do.

Scotty arrived beside us, also casting long glances into the sky, searching for incoming enemy planes.

"London took another terrible hammering last night," he said.

"Our only hope is that the Jerries will overstretch themselves," said Tug thoughtfully. "Bombing day and night, it must be wearing their pilots out."

"Maybe they'll give themselves a rest today?" said Scotty hopefully.

It was a thing we all said many times, and it always seemed to work like a bad-luck charm. As so many times before, the sound of the siren told us that today was not going to be a quiet day. We were already out of our chairs and heading for our planes as the voice of control came over the loudspeaker: "All pilots in the air. Repeat. All pilots in the air. Attack fleet coming."

I reflected on his "All pilots in the air" instead of just scrambling one or two sections. It must be a huge attack force on its way. And it was.

We ran into them just south-east of London at 14,000 feet: a huge armada of planes. The sky was black with them.

As I saw the lines of bombers with their fighter escorts, pictures of London flashed through my mind, things that I had seen of the damage done by the bombs the previous day and night: the dead bodies, the wreckage, the flattened buildings. I vowed that these German bombers would have to fight hard to get past me again.

The sky was now full of planes. As well as our two squadrons from Hornchurch, 327 and 58, we had been joined by other Fighter Command Group 11 Squadrons from the Rochford and Manston bases in north Kent. Hawker Hurricanes and Spitfires from those bases now flew with us as we united against this formidable enemy armada of planes: the bombers – Heinkels, Dorniers and Stukas – and their Messerschmitt 109 fighter guards. All told there must have been 200 German planes heading towards us, the biggest air attack I'd yet encountered. The sheer size of it almost took my breath away. Luckily, there was no time for any of us to dwell on it.

"Plenty for everyone, chaps!" came the voice of our squadron leader over my R-T headphones. "Let's go! Free attack! Just hit the blighters!"

The danger with so many planes in the air was of hitting another plane. There are no brakes in the sky – if you found yourself heading on a collision course you just had to change direction, and hope that didn't put you in the path of yet another plane.

We dodged their Me109s as best we could and poured tracer after tracer of bullets into those German bombers. Just hitting a German bomber was no guarantee that it would go down. They were well built, I'll say that much for them.

Soon the blue sky was thickly patterned with black-and-white criss-crosses of smoke from zooming fighters, and burning planes falling from the sky. With this much chaos in the air there was no time to take pause and try and keep a tally of who had shot down what, it was just fly, fire, hit, run, fly back and fire and hit again.

I flew over one of the Heinkels, strafing it with a burst of machine-gun fire as I did so, and then turned for my return attack. Out of the corner of my eye I saw an Me109 coming straight for me from behind. I dived in time and the Messerschmitt's burst of machine-gun fire flew over my head, chipping bits off the hood of my canopy as it did so.

I climbed back up to get a height advantage. As I did so, I saw Tug in Green 1 zoom past me. He turned and gave me a wave and a thumbs-up.

Suddenly, directly in front of him and just above him, I saw an Me109 that had been hit crashing down out of the sky, flame and black smoke pouring from its nose. It was on a direct course to collide with Tug's flight path. Frantically I pointed and Tug looked up. He saw the falling Messerschmitt and put his Spitfire into an abrupt dive, banking heavily at the same time. But it was too late: the burning plane hit one of Tug's wings with a crash, tearing it off.

Immediately his plane went into a spin, spiralling down out of the sky. I tore after him, ready to cover him against the other enemy planes if he tried to bail out. I saw him trying to slide back the hood of his cockpit, but it had stuck, just the same as had happened to me when my plane had crashed.

Suddenly an Me109 came out of nowhere from behind me. The first I knew of it was a tracer of bullets hurtling past me and smashing into Tug's plane. As I watched, Tug threw up his arms, and then his plane just blew up, exploding in mid-air, throwing out flames and gases and bits of fuselage.

I turned to go after the Messerschmitt that had got Tug, but one of the Hurricanes was already on to it. The Hurricane pilot put a burst into the rear of the Messerschmitt, tearing off its rudder, and the German fighter plunged into a spin, fire and smoke belching out from its tail end.

A second or so later the Messerschmitt pilot bailed out, his parachute blossoming out wide as he began to float down towards the ground. For a moment I was tempted to let him have it right there, let my bullets tear into him as he drifted in the sky, but I stopped myself. It was one of those unwritten rules of aerial combat. You only shot at a man when he was in his plane, you didn't hit him when he was dangling helpless from a parachute in the sky. Not even if he'd just killed your friend.

By this time the German fighter planes must have begun to run low on fuel because they all began to turn, heading out towards the sea. The large bombers, left otherwise with no escorts to protect them, also turned. What was left of the German air fleet, about 150 planes, began their journey home.

"Back to base, chaps!" came the voice of our squadron leader in my headphones.

I turned my plane and headed back to Hornchurch. As I flew I counted the planes that were left of the 24 Spitfires of 327 and 58 Squadrons that had set out just half an hour before. There were sixteen of us. Eight down. Some of those would have parachuted to safety, or bought their damaged plane down to ground somewhere in the countryside below. But not Tug Banks. Tug Banks was dead.

Invasion Alert

That evening I was sitting in the mess hall, drinking a cup of tea. I'd left my meal half-finished; I just didn't feel like eating. Scotty, too, just pushed his food around the plate. We both felt badly about Tug buying it, but somehow neither of us felt like putting it into words, apart from the occasional "Poor old Tug."

I was just about to go out for a walk to try to get my feelings sorted out, when our squadron leader, Jerry Payne, head of Red Section came into the mess. He walked over to me and clapped me on the shoulder. He was still dressed in his flying kit.

"Acker wants a word with you," he said. "He's waiting for you in his office."

"What does he want?" I asked.

"I'll let the wingco tell you himself," he said. "Don't keep him waiting, there's a good fellow. Chop-chop."

I left my tea half-drunk and hurried across the base to the wing commander's office.

Wing Commander "Acker" Atkinson was busy writing at his desk as I tapped at his half-open door. He was a grizzled old character, a veteran of the First War. Tough, but fair.

He motioned me to come in.

"You sent for me, sir?" I said, standing to attention before him.

"At ease, Smith," said Acker. "You're not on the carpet for anything. In fact, the exact opposite. I've just been discussing the situation over your Green Section with Jerry Payne. I'm sorry about Banks, he was a damned fine pilot and a great section leader."

"The best there was, sir," I said. "I was proud to have flown with him. He saved my bacon on a number of occasions when I was first up, cutting out the Hun plenty of times when they could have taken me out."

"I know," nodded Atkinson soberly. "The thing is, we need a new leader of Green Section, and Payne and I think you're the man for the job. As of this moment you're promoted to flight lieutenant."

I suppose I should have seen it coming. With fewer and fewer experienced pilots able to go up, it had to be one of the existing members of the squadron. It still felt a bit sour to me, though, promotion by Dead Man's Shoes, as we called it, especially when the Dead Man had been a good friend.

"Thank you, sir," I said. "I shall do my best to live up to your confidence in me."

"You'd better," smiled Acker, "we need your experience up there."

"Will I be getting a third pilot for Green Section?" I asked. "Or will it be just me and McBurn?"

"Command have promised me a third pilot for you by first thing tomorrow morning. I don't know his name yet, but we'll find out by Assembly Call. There's a briefing of all officers first thing tomorrow morning, 0500 hours. Early start tomorrow. You'd better get some sleep."

He stood up behind his desk and saluted.

"Dismiss, Flight Lieutenant Smith."

I returned his salute.

"Thank you, sir," I said.

By the time I got back to the mess hall, Jerry Payne had already told everyone the news about my promotion, and there was much slapping me on the back, and murmurs of "Well done, young 'un. You deserved it," and similar sentiments from the older and more experienced pilots. Proud though I was of my promotion, it was still tinged with sadness that I'd earned it at the death of a friend.

I accepted a congratulatory drink from young Scotty. Then I hung about in the mess just long enough not to offend all the other chaps who wanted to buy me a drink in celebration. Once things had quietened down a bit I sloped quietly off, with a murmured goodnight to Scotty. His nod showed me that he understood that I wanted to be on my own.

Outside the mess I looked up at the night sky. At the stars. At our battleground. And sadly I reflected that tomorrow there'd be one less great pilot flying up there. Another friend gone.

Five o'clock the next morning, 15 September, found the section leaders from 327 and 58 Squadron sitting attentively in the Briefing Room. For the very first time, I was one of them. Acker Atkinson finished chalking a rough map on the blackboard. It showed the coast of northern France, and that of southern England.

"Right, chaps," he said. "All of you are familiar with this. You've flown over it often enough. The difference today is that – if our Intelligence reports are right, and it looks as if they are – you're all in for the biggest battle of your lives, and instructions have come down from the top brass to tell you why. They think it's only fair, and I agree with them."

He picked up his pointer and tapped along the chalked outline of the French coast.

"The German invasion fleet has now been ready here for some days. According to Intelligence reports there are 3,000 boats there, all ready to cross, with 30 German divisions. If they don't land here by late September then the tides will be against them and the invasion will have to be postponed. Possibly even cancelled altogether. But the Germans can't invade until they're sure we're out of the way.

"Apparently Goering had promised Hitler that the RAF would be completely smashed by the start of September and the way would be clear for the invasion by then. Two weeks later, and we're still here, to his immense distress and annoyance.

"Our Intelligence people believe the Germans will now throw everything they've got at us, starting today. I don't believe I am exaggerating when I say that you are all that stands between victory or defeat in this war. We have to defeat the Luftwaffe in the air today, and over the next few days. If we lose, then the Nazis will have the final piece in their jigsaw map that is Europe."

He looked at his watch.

"It is now 0530 hours. The enemy are expected to launch their attack within the next two hours. Prepare your men, prepare your planes, and good luck."

I headed towards the mess hall to grab a bite of breakfast before the balloon went up. Not too much food, of course – it didn't do you good to have your stomach overfilled when you were being thrown this way and that way, sometimes even upside down, during the course of an air battle. As I walked in I saw Scotty talking to a young, fresh-faced, red-haired kid still dressed in his blues.

"Bonzo, this is Stephen Byways," Scotty introduced us. "Byways, this is our section leader, Flight Lieutenant John Smith."

"Pilot Byways reporting, sir," said the boy, and he saluted as he stood stiffly to attention. "I've been assigned to Green Section of 327 Squadron."

"Relax," I said.

It made me feel a little uncomfortable. Here was this young lad standing to attention, saluting me and calling me "sir". It made me feel as if I was about fifty years old instead of nineteen. Out of the corner of my eye I saw Scotty grin at my obvious discomfort.

"How old are you?" I asked.

"Eighteen and a half," he said. He added: "I've been fully trained."

"Good," I said. "Have you got your flying kit?"

"Not yet, skipper," he said.

"He's only just arrived," explained Scotty. "He came down by lorry last night with the new intake."

"OK," I said. "Scotty, take Byways to the stores and get him kitted out. Then fix him up with his plane and let him get used to it. Then, when he's all ready, he can come in and have some breakfast." I gave the young lad a smile, so he didn't think I was being too hard on him. "I'm not being mean, but if the scramble suddenly goes, it's easier for you to run to your plane from the breakfast table than have to start getting your flying kit on."

"Roger, skipper," Byways nodded. He looked deadly serious as he said it.

"Come on, let's get you fixed up," said Scotty.

I watched them go, and thought how much older we must all look to Byways. Battle does that to men, it puts years on their faces.

After breakfast, I sat outside the mess hall in my deckchair. When Scotty returned with our latest recruit, Byways now had the regulation pilot's flying gear on: light brown leather jacket over a blue pullover, the lot.

"Excellent," I said. "Get some chow and then sit out here while Scotty and I tell you how to save your life while fighting Jerry up in the blue yonder."

On his return, Scotty and I gave the boy what advice we

could about what he would need to know when the German attack came.

I let him have the same pep talk that I'd given Scotty when he'd joined our squadron, about not letting yourself be caught out and blinded by the sun, about watching your back, about doing his very best not to panic. However, as I sat there I could only think: "Nothing we can say will help this boy when it happens. We can't fly his plane for him. If he panics when the fighting starts and puts his plane into a wrong direction, or dives or climbs too sharply and blacks out, there's nothing I can do to help him." When you're a fighter pilot, you're on your own. Finally all I could do was pat him on the shoulder in what I hoped was a comforting gesture and tell him: "Do your best to stay alive up there and just hit the opposition as hard and as often as you can."

From then on, we waited. There was a definite sense that today was going to be something special. It was as if all the previous weeks of battles in the air had been leading up to this: the final struggle. I imagined that at every airfield across England the same scene was being played out: pilots sitting around, all kitted up, planes at the ready. Checking their watches. Making jokes about the enemy being late, but everyone feeling that today there was just that little bit more tension in the air, just that bit extra tight knot of fear in the stomach.

0800 came and went. No sign of the enemy. The loudspeakers remained silent. Maybe they weren't coming today? Maybe it was tomorrow? Or maybe Hitler had decided to cancel the invasion altogether? Wild thoughts like these passed through our heads, even though we knew they were out of the question. Too much was at stake. The battle had been fought too long and too hard, with too many losses, for the final chapter to be avoided.

0830, and still no sign. No radar warnings. Nothing.

The minutes ticked by. For heaven's sake, I thought, hurry up. This waiting is worse than the fighting! Looking at the tense faces of the other pilots, I knew they felt the same as I did, even the older hands. Byways, who was going up into battle for the first time, could barely sit still. Every now and then he got up and walked about, and then sat down again.

0845. Still no sign. They surely had to come soon or the day would be nearly over.

0850. By now the airfield was so heavy with silence you could almost have heard a pin drop. And still there was silence from the loudspeakers. No call to scramble. No word of the enemy.

At 0900 hours we finally got the call. "Scramble all planes. Enemy approaching." As we ran to our planes we almost cheered with relief. At last!

At 0915 we ran into them coming over the east coast at

12,000 feet. Intelligence had been right about the size of this attack, it was the biggest force I'd seen. The sight was just absolutely staggering. There were about 400 German fighters protecting about 200 bombers. The sky was black with German planes.

"Green Section, stay close to me in V-formation," I told Scotty and Byways over the R-T.

"Read that, skipper," they both responded.

We were in a pack now: spread out from north of the Thames right down to the south coast, there must have been at least 200 Spitfires and Hurricanes in the air. Our forces were from every station, from both Fighter Commands 11 and 12. We may have been a formidable force, but we all knew we were heavily outnumbered.

I went into the attack straight away, leading Scotty and Byways behind me as I headed for the nearest bomber, a Dornier.

"I'll take the Me109, you two hit the bomber," I said. "Go for the pilot at the front."

I headed straight for the Me109 that was riding shotgun for the Dornier on the near side, firing all guns, heading straight towards it, head-on on a collision course. The Messerschmitt decided I was obviously mad enough to commit suicide this way and wasn't going to change direction, because he went into a climb.

I turned as sharply as I could and followed him. As he began to turn to look for me, I caught him in my sights, and let fire with a tracer that tore his starboard wing apart.

Out of the corner of my eye I saw Scotty and Byways still attacking the glazed front of the Dornier, weaving two criss-crossing trails of white smoke in the air as they dodged the machine-gun fire from the bomber's forward gun. There was no doubt about Byways's flying ability or his courage. Young as he was, he flew at the bomber and hit it again and again, until the glass was so cracked I knew it had to go. I also knew from experience that the crew behind the glass were either dead, or badly wounded. Sure enough, a few seconds later, the Dornier began to go down. One less bomber.

The sky was filled with similar battles going on. The Germans had sent over enough fighter planes this time to allow some of them to be released to engage our Spitfires and Hurricanes in individual combat without leaving their bombers unguarded, and all around individual dogfights were going on. Every few moments there was an explosion nearby with black smoke from another wrecked aircraft.

Planes filled the sky. Smoke obscured our vision. Time and time again I saw two planes crash into each other in mid-air collision and burst into flames. It was just mayhem and madness, and all we could do was fly and dodge and weave and attack and hope we wouldn't crash into anything.

After about twenty minutes of this the sweat was pouring down my face and my helmet felt sticky, despite the altitude. I could understand why some pilots preferred not to wear goggles in case they misted up.

I did my best to keep an eye out for Scotty and Byways, but it was almost impossible in the clutter of planes whirling around the smoke-filled sky. Finally some of the German planes began to turn back as they ran low on fuel. Jerry Payne's voice came over the R-T ordering our squadron back to Hornchurch for refuelling.

"Back to base, 327!" he chirped. "They'll be back. Plenty more for later. Time to fuel up."

We dropped back to base, leaving 58 Squadron in the sky with many of the other fighters who were still attacking and harassing the German planes that had stayed. Once we were refuelled we'd go up and carry on the defence in the air, and 58 could come down.

While the ground crew refuelled my plane, I hurried to meet our newest pilot as his plane taxied in. He tumbled out of his cockpit and lifted his goggles.

"Well done, Byways!" I congratulated him. "You showed you've got guts and skill up there just now. Hang on to those two and you'll be OK."

"Thanks, skipper!" he said with a nervous smile. "It's pretty crowded up there, isn't it?"

"It's busier than usual today," I said. "You joined on a bad day."

"No," grinned Byways. "This is a good day. What's the point of being a fighter if no one turns up to fight you?"

"True," I said. "But don't get too confident. We're not fighting amateurs up there, you know. These Germans are experienced and battle-hardened. Get too cocky and make one mistake, and you'll be dead."

"Point taken, skip," nodded Byways. "Thanks."

Then we were refuelled, and went up into the air again.

And that was how it went on all that day. More German fighters, more German bombers, and us in the skies doing our best to stop them reaching London, or stop them reaching our air bases. For so long it just seemed like a never-ending nightmare. As fast as we shot them down, so more German planes appeared.

By the time we went up for our fourth defensive foray, with still no sign of the German attack lessening, we were beginning to get exhausted, both physically and mentally. The sky was now a mixture of cloud and burning smoke. Even in the cockpit and with a mask on, you could taste it, acrid and choking.

As we went up we saw a wave of twenty Dorniers and Heinkels coming in over the east coast with their Me109 escorts at 10,000 feet. Twenty Me109s and twenty bombers. Forty planes in all.

Behind them was a wave of at least another thirty Stukas, followed by another twenty Messerschmitts. Behind *them*, at least another 400 planes. The German attack seemed to be endless.

The thought of the heavy bombers devastating London again filled me with a cold anger. I checked that Scotty and Byways were close to me and asked our squadron leader for permission to take Green Section to attack the bombers.

"All yours, Green Section," came Jerry Payne's voice over my R-T. "We'll take the Stukas."

"Green Section, with me," I said.

Scotty and Byways followed me as we broke away from the rest of our squadron. Outnumbered forty to three, there was no way we could go for a head-on attack, so I flew in an arc which took us behind the first wave of bombers and fighters. While Red and Blue Sections joined the other squadrons in attacking the next formation, Green Section went in hard on the tails of the first German wave.

I set my sights on the Dornier at the rear of the German column. Even as I let fly with a burst of tracer, the bomber's Messerschmitt escort turned to intercept me. Before he could get a fix on me, Byways came at him, flying so close to it that for a moment I thought he was going to crash into the German fighter. Byways's bullets smashed into the front of the German fighter, destroying his engine and his propeller. Meanwhile, Scotty and I had both hit the Dornier with bursts into its tailplane, and the bomber lurched abruptly in the sky, and then its tailplane flew off, and the huge aircraft tipped and dropped. Two down.

From then on it was fight and fly, bullets pouring from our guns into them, and flying dangerously past our planes. Time stopped there in the sky; there was just gunfire, explosions, smoke, and machines whirling and swooping.

Four of the Messerschmitts riding shotgun had decided that we needed to be dealt with, and they turned in a loop and came straight for us.

"Up, Green 2 and 3!" I ordered.

Scotty and Byways soared up, while I headed swiftly down. I turned, and then came up from underneath and let one of them have a burst of fire in its belly. I banked and came back and hit another side-on, raking along its side. Meanwhile, Scotty and Byways had swooped down on the other two, hitting them both from above, their bullets ripping along the fuselage of each fighter from the tailplane to the propeller.

"Right, let's get the bombers!" I said. "Break formation. Don't let them get a fix on you."

We flew wide of each other, and then came in on the bombers from three different directions, guns firing. The German machine-gunners opened up and a burst from one of the Heinkels tore jagged holes in my perspex hood, missing my head by inches. Our sudden attack had thrown them, though, and we hit two of the bombers at once, the engines of both planes bursting into flames and sending the huge machines spiralling down to earth.

By now the Germans' fuel was running low and the survivors of this wave turned their planes and headed for home. We chased them out over the sea, firing at them all the time. Then we turned and flew back to join the rest of our squadron, ready to face the next attack.

And still the Germans came, wave after wave of them.

By six o'clock that evening we hadn't had time to stop for a bite to eat, just a quick cup of tea from a mobile urn when we'd scrambled down from the cockpits of our planes for refuelling.

As the light faded from the sky and the last wave of daylight raiders returned home across the Channel, we flew back to our bases to count our losses and leave the defences to the night-time forces: the anti-aircraft guns and the barrage balloons.

I felt bone-weary as I clambered down from my Spitfire that last time. We had kept the enemy at bay this day one more time.

I checked that Scotty and Byways landed safely, and then headed towards the Operations Room to report Green Section's tally of kills for the day.

Afterwards, as I walked toward the mess hut to finally grab something to eat, I found myself being hailed by Crusty Pearson.

What is it now? I thought. Crusty Pearson always meant trouble of some sort.

"There's a visitor for you, Smith," Crusty announced crisply. "In the wing commander's outer office. You'd better get over there."

I was frowning as I reached the wing commander's hut. Who on earth could be visiting me? And why? I found out as I opened the door and went in. There, standing alone inside the hut, was my father.

For once he wasn't standing in that military stance he always had, that stiff-back chest-out parade-ground pose. He looked suddenly old, his shoulders sagging slightly. The thought hit me in an instant: he'd come to tell me that something terrible had happened to Ma. She'd been killed in the bombing.

Alive!

"Hello, Pa," I said, steeling myself for the bad news. To help him say it better, I asked: "Is it Ma?"

He shook his head. "No, John. Your ma's fine. And so's Edward."

Edward? I stared at him, stunned, and then I could feel a grin spread all over my face. Edward was alive!

"That's wonderful news!" I blurted out. But I was puzzled. If it was all good news, what had brought him all the way out to Hornchurch. And why did he look so … unhappy? The answer came with his next few words, and he limped over to me and stood facing me, his shoulders now going back. It was as if he had made a difficult decision.

"John," he said, "I've come to say sorry. Your ma said I could write it in a letter, but I wanted to come and tell you face to face."

"Sorry?" I repeated, bewildered. This wasn't like my father at all.

"For the things I said and the way I acted," he said. "I was unfair towards you. And towards the RAF. You didn't deserve it. And the RAF didn't deserve it. I was quite wrong."

"Well…" I began, feeling stuck for words, not knowing what to say. This was all coming completely out of the blue.

Pa handed me an envelope.

"We'll talk in a minute," he said. "First, read this. It's from Edward. I came to give you this so you'd know yourself he's all right." He hesitated, and then he added, "I'll wait for you outside." He gave a self-conscious smile. "I always have preferred showdowns in the open air."

I took the envelope from Pa and watched him limp out of the wingco's office. Then I took out the letter and read what Edward had written.

"Dear Ma and Pa", Edward began. "Well, I guess I've caused you a lot of worry. I'm writing this from up here somewhere on the coast of Scotland. I've just landed from a trawler. The first thing I heard when I got in touch with my unit was that I was officially dead, so I thought I'd get this off to you straight away to let you know that I'm not. I tried phoning you but the Post Office say your phone is out of order." I smiled at that, wondering what Edward would say when he found out that it wasn't just the phone, it was the whole house that was out of order. The letter went on to describe how he'd been wounded and had hidden out. Then he said:

"All the time, though, I was getting word about what was happening back in Blighty, and about the terrible hammering the Jerry bombers have been giving you. Everyone in Norway and up here in Scotland is talking about what a magnificent job our RAF boys are doing keeping Hitler's flying circus at bay. Heroes, every one of them, in my opinion. And that includes John. If you see him, give him my love and tell him I admire what he and his fellow boys in blue are doing enormously. I'm sure you've been telling him this all along, Pa, but be careful about giving John too much praise. We don't want him to get a big head just because he's a hero."

I looked up from Edward's letter and out through the window to where my father was standing on the grass, with his back to me, looking at the planes and the waiting air crews. I wondered how he must have felt when he read that phrase of Edward's about not praising me too much, in the light of the insults he'd thrown at me. I returned to Edward's letter.

"I hear that Winnie – all right, Pa, Winston Churchill, I know you don't approve of me being disrespectful about our prime minister, even if it's done with affection – I hear that Mr Churchill gave John and the other RAF fighter pilots the biggest praise when he said of them, 'Never in the field of human conflict has so much been owed by so many to so few.' Just about sums it up, eh?

"Anyway, enough of all this. I look forward to seeing you both soon. All my love, your loving son, Edward."

I folded the letter up, put it back in the envelope, and then went out to where Pa was waiting for me. I handed Edward's letter back to Pa.

"I'm so glad he's safe," I said. "I'll try and get some leave and get home when he does."

"Your mother would like that," said Pa. Then he added, "I would like that." He shook his head, still looking guilty, and continued: "I was blind about what a good job you were doing, John. All of you flying boys. I don't know whether it was because I was still upset you didn't go into the Fusiliers, or worry over Edward being missing, or a combination of many things. All I know is, I was wrong. It took a letter from one of my sons to make me realize how proud I was of both of you. Can you forgive me?"

In that moment I wanted to go to Pa and give him a big hug, the way I used to when Edward and I were very small, but I knew that would be going too far for him. He was an old soldier, a colonel, and I was his son, the airman. And we were on public view.

"There's nothing to forgive, Pa," I said. "But I can't tell you what it means to hear you say it, and to know that you came all the way out here." I smiled in an effort to try and lighten the moment. "To an RAF base."

Pa caught the mood and gave me a smile back. He held out his hand, and I took it firmly in mine.

"Here's to the army and the RAF," he said.

Here's to the family, Pa," I said. "Together."

THE BATTLE OF BRITAIN AND AFTER

The Blitz of London by the German Luftwaffe continued until early November 1940, a total of 57 days of continual bombing from 7 September. There was just one break during the otherwise constant bombing of the capital; on 2 November the weather was too bad for the German aircraft to take to the skies. London was not the only British city to be a victim of the German tactic of aerial Blitzkrieg. On 14 November, Coventry was devastated by German bombers, and then Southampton, Birmingham, Cardiff, Swansea, Liverpool, Plymouth, Portsmouth, Bristol, Glasgow, Belfast and many other towns. During these bombing raids, which continued until May 1941, German air attacks killed 40,000 British civilians, injured another 46,000, and damaged more than a million homes.

However, the Battle of Britain itself culminated on 15 September 1940. That day – now remembered as Battle of Britain Day – saw the last major attack by the Luftwaffe against the RAF, a last ditch attempt to destroy the RAF and clear the way for the sea invasion.

On 16 September bad weather prevented the Luftwaffe from launching another large-scale air attack, and on 17 September turbulent winds again prevented an attack. It was also now doubtful if the Luftwaffe could launch a further decisive attack anyway. Following the sustained period of air battles with the RAF over England, the German pilots were exhausted, spares for their planes were in short supply, bomber units were depleted, and morale was at a low ebb. They had been assured by German Intelligence that the RAF had hardly any fighter planes left to oppose them, and yet 15 September had seen 300 RAF fighter planes in action against them over the southern counties of England.

On 17 September, most historians believe, as a direct result of the failure of the Luftwaffe to destroy the RAF by 15 September, Adolf Hitler postponed Operation Sea Lion. Two days later he gave the order for the German invasion fleet to be dispersed. Britain had avoided the imminent threat of invasion.

Between 7 September and 30 September the Luftwaffe lost 380 aircraft against RAF losses of 178. In the words of Winston Churchill, Britain's wartime prime minister, when praising the RAF for saving Britain from invasion: "Never in the field of human conflict has so much been owed by so many to so few."

THE SIGNIFICANCE OF THE BATTLE OF BRITAIN

The resistance shown by the British during the Battle of Britain had a threefold effect:

- It stopped the Germans from being able to launch their invasion of Britain, which would have ended the war in 1940 and given Hitler complete domination of Europe.

- It raised the morale of the British people, and of others throughout the world, who now saw that Hitler's military might could be defeated.

- It led to Hitler turning his attention away from invading Britain and instead invading Russia. This led to Russia being brought into the war on the side of the Allies, a major cause in the final defeat of Nazi Germany.

THE AIRCRAFT OF THE BATTLE OF BRITAIN

BRITISH (RAF)

VICKERS SUPERMARINE SPITFIRE Mk I to V

Engine: One 1478hp (1102kW) Rolls-Royce Merlin 45 12-cylinder Vee engine
Armament: Eight 0.303inch fixed forward-firing machine guns in the leading edges of the wings
Speed: 594 km/h (394mph)
Climb rate: 1204m (3950 feet) per minute
Ceiling: 11,125m (36,500ft)
Range: 1827km (1,135 miles)
Weight: empty: 2267kg (4998lb)
Max load for take-off: 2911kg (6,417lb)
Span: 11.23m (36ft 10in)
Length: 9.12m (29ft 11in)
Height: 3.02m (9ft 11in)

The Supermarine Spitfire was the most agile plane flown in the Battle of Britain. It could even outmanoeuvre the Messerschmitt Me109E. Another element that gave the Spitfire its superiority was in its eight wing-mounted Browning machine guns, which, even though they were out-ranged by the German cannon, had a decisive concentration of rounds per second.

HAWKER HURRICANE SINGLE SEATER FIGHTER Mk II

Engine: One 1460hp (1088kW) Rolls-Royce Merlin XX 12-cylinder Vee engine
Armament: Two 40mm fixed forward-firing cannon under the wing, and two 0.303 inch fixed firing forward machine guns in the leading edges of the wings
Speed: 518 km/h (322mph)
Climb rate: to 6095m (20,000ft) in 12 minutes 24 seconds
Ceiling: 9785m (32,100ft)
Range: 1448km (900 miles)
Weight: empty: 2586kg (5700lb)
Max load for take-off: 3674kg (8100lb)
Span: 12.19m (40ft)
Length: 9.81m (32ft 2.25in)
Height: 3.98m (13ft 1in)

The Hurricane was Britain's first monoplane fighter. Although it was later replaced by the Spitfire, many fighter pilots who flew aerial combat in both planes preferred the Hurricane because the sloping nose gave better forward vision than the long nose of the Spitfire. The pilots also liked the sturdy build of the machine: as a fighter plane it was solid and reliable and could take quite a bit of punishment, and its sturdy and wider undercarriage made it easier to land than the narrower Spitfire.

GERMAN (LUFTWAFFE)

MESSERSCHMITT Bf 109E-1 to E-4

Engine: One 1175hp (876kW) Daimler-Benz D8 601Aa 12-cylinder inverted Vee engine
Armament: Two 20mm fixed forward-firing cannon under the wing, and two 7.92mm fixed firing forward machine guns in the upper part of the forward fuselage
Speed: 560 km/h (348mph)
Climb rate: to 6000m (19,685ft) in 7 minutes 45 seconds
Ceiling: 10500m (34,450ft)
Range: 660km (410 miles)
Weight: empty: 2125kg (4685lb)
Max load for take-off: 2665kg (5875lb)
Span: 9.87m (32ft 4in)
Length: 8.64m (28ft 4.5in)
Height: 2.50m (8ft 2.33in)

This plane was known as the "Emil" to German pilots. It was as fast as the Spitfire. Although not as manoeuvrable as the Spitfire, it was more manoeuvrable that the Hawker Hurricane. The Me109 had the ability to be able to out-dive both the Hurricane and the Spitfire. Its 20mm guns fired at slower rate than either of its two opposing British fighter planes, and although the weapons had greater penetrating power, it demanded more skill to achieve decisive damage. The plane's narrow undercarriage and long wheel struts also gave pilots some problems as it led to some instability while taxiing forward.

HEINKEL MEDIUM BOMBER He 111H and He 111HZ

Engine: Two 1350hp (1007kW) Junkers Jumo 211F-2 12-cylinder engines.
Armament: One 7.92mm fixed firing forward machine gun in a nose position; one 7.92mm machine gun in a dorsal position; one 7.92mm machine gun in rear of ventral gondola; two 7.92mm machine guns in each of two beam positions; and one 7.92mm fixed machine gun in the tail cone; plus a bomb load of 2500kg (5511lb)
Speed: 405 km/h (252mph)
Climb rate: to 4000m (13,125ft) in 23 minutes 30 seconds
Ceiling: 8500m (27,890ft)
Range: 1930km (1199 miles)
Weight: empty: 8680kg (19,136lb)
Max load for take-off: 14000kg (30,865lb)
Span: 22.60m (74ft 1.75in)
Length: 16.40m (53ft 9.5in)
Height: 3.40m (13ft 1.5in)

The Heinkel He-111 was the standard Luftwaffe bomber at the time of the Battle of Britain. It was ideal as a medium-range bomber for attacks on countries close to Germany, but was disadvantaged by the distance it had to travel to reach targets in England. Among its features was a retractable ventral firing point beneath the plane, in which a gunner sat.

DORNIER LIGHT BOMBER Do 17E

Engine: Two 750hp (559kW) BMW VI 7.3 12-cylinder Vee engines
Armament: One 7.92mm trainable forward-firing machine gun in starboard side of the cockpit; provision for one 7.92mm trainable forward-firing machine gun in the lower nose; one 7.92mm trainable forward-firing machine gun in rear of the cockpit; one 7.92mm rearward-firing machine gun; plus a bomb load of 750kg (16531lb)
Speed: 355 km/h (221mph)
Climb rate: not available
Ceiling: 5100m (16,730ft)
Range: 500km (311 miles)
Weight: empty: 4500kg (992lb)
Max load for take-off: 7040kg (15,520lb)
Span: 18m (59ft 0.67in)
Length: 16.25m (53ft 3.5in)
Height: 4.32m (14ft 2in)

The Dornier D-17 first saw service during the Spanish Civil War. Its weak points against attacks were from above and below. Because of its narrow fuselage it was known as "The Flying Pencil". Its shape was similar to that of the British Hampden bomber. As a result many of the British Hampden bombers were fired at by their own anti-aircraft guns which mistook them for the D-17.

JUNKERS Ju 88A, D, H, S & T

Engine: Two 1340hp (999kW) Junkers Jumo 211J-1/2 12-cylinder engines.

Armament: One 7.92mm fixed or trainable forward-firing machine gun in windscreen; one 13mm or two 7.92mm forward-firing machine guns in nose position; two 7.92mm machine gun in rear of cockpit; and one 13mm or two 7.92 trainable rearward firing machine guns in rear of undernose gondola; plus a bomb load of 2500kg (5511lb)

Speed: 470 km/h (292mph)

Climb rate: to 5400m (17,715ft) in 23 minutes

Ceiling: 8200mm (26,900ft)

Range: 2730km (1696 miles)

Weight: empty: 9860kg (21,737lb)

Max load for take-off: 14000kg (30,865lb)

Span: 20m (65ft 7.5in)

Length: 14.40m (47ft 2.75in)

Height: 485m (15ft 11in)

The Junkers 88 was the most versatile aircraft in the German air fleet. It served as a level bomber, as a dive-bomber, and as a night fighter. It was also used for reconnaissance flights. It was used by the Luftwaffe as a medium bomber during the Battle of Britain. However, it was no match for the Spitfires or the Hurricanes.

TANK ATTACK

DISASTER IN THE DESERT

In June 1940, Italy declared war on Britain and threatened to invade her territories in North Africa. During the summer of that year there were several skirmishes between the British 7th Armoured Division and Italian units. Then, in September 1940, the Italian army (250,000 strong) under Marshal Graziani crossed the desert and occupied key towns in Egypt (at that time a British protectorate).

Under the command of General Wavell, a British force of 30,000 men retaliated and cut off the Italian army. There followed five months of fighting in which British, Australian and South African forces pushed the Italian infantry back, forcing them to surrender in February 1941. It looked like the Allies had won the war in the North African desert.

However, Hitler offered the Italian leader, Mussolini, a German armoured division to help continue the battle. The offer was accepted and shortly afterwards the first German units arrived under the brilliant command of General Rommel – the

Desert Fox, as he became known. So began a long series of battles between the Allies – including troops from Australia, New Zealand, South Africa, Rhodesia (now Zimbabwe), India and other friendly countries and the Axis forces (Germany and Italy).

In March 1941, Rommel launched his first major offensive against the Allies. It was a success and pushed the British right back into Egypt. German forces also laid siege to Tobruk. In June, British troops under Wavell tried to break through the German defences and recover the captured area of Cyrenaica. This counter-attack failed.

During the winter, many battles were fought, with the Allies losing out to Rommel and his Afrika Korps. Sensing the possibility of an unthinkable defeat, in June 1941 the British appointed Sir Claude Auchinleck as the new commander of the Allied forces, now called the Eighth Army.

In November 1941, Auchinleck mounted his first major desert offensive: he raised the siege of Tobruk and recovered Cyrenaica. This success was short lived, as by February 1942 Rommel's forces had pushed the Eighth Army back again to the Gazala Line. Worse was to come in the summer of that year.

Rommel destroyed the Eighth Army's armour in the

Battle of Gazala and then went on to take Tobruk and invade Egypt.

The British dug in at Alamein and managed to repel a series of German attacks. However, the situation still looked desperate. As a final throw of the dice, in August 1942 a new general was brought in, Sir Harold Alexander, along with a new commander for the Eighth Army, General Bernard Montgomery – or Monty, as he became known. Montgomery stated that there would be no more retreats: the Eighth Army would fight and win, or it would die fighting.

Our story starts in July 1942, just before the new commander arrives. A young tank driver prepares for action.

First Battle

I'll never forget the first time I heard a Stuka. Six of them came screaming down from the sky at 300 mph. It was a late afternoon towards the end of July in 1942. I'd only spent a day at the front when our position was attacked. Bullets from machine guns tore into our tents. I heard the terrifying whine of descending bombs. For a second, I was just too shocked to move. Then I threw myself into the shelter of a dugout, just as a bomb hit our petrol dump, sending flames and thick smoke into the air. This was it. I was at war.

Whistles sounded. Burning embers from the steel drums started to rain down around me, falling, smouldering, like a toxic hailstorm. There was a deafening roar as the tanks started up. And more gunfire. Some of it near, from our own anti-aircraft guns. Some, more distant: the Germans had opened fire with their big guns. Soon their Panzers would be the horizon, launching their shells against our positions.

"Come on, Smith!" yelled Lieutenant Weston. "Get the old girl going!"

Smith. That was me. Driver John Smith of the Tank Regiment. Nineteen years old, just arrived in the desert, and already I was about to go into battle. The "old girl" was our tank, a Crusader. I joined the rest of the crew, ran for our tank standing in formation, and clambered up the metal side panel, using the caterpillar tracks as a ladder.

Once inside, I fired up the engine. The Crusader may have been built for many things, but it wasn't designed to be comfortable. Three men – driver, radio operator and machine-gunner – squashed down below into a stinking hot metal box, with the tank commander and the gunner up in the turret. Once the hatch was closed there was even less room because the commander had to drop down into the hull.

Our radio operator, Fred Read, nicknamed Prof because everyone thought he was brainy, gave me a friendly pat on the shoulder as he slipped into his position at the back of the tank.

"Don't worry, John," he said, "the Germans are miles away."

I forced a grin into my face, though I didn't really feel like smiling. This was my first time in a real battle. True, we'd been on exercises back in England where they'd tried to make it as convincing as possible with live ammunition and exploding flares. But this was different: this was the real thing.

My stomach felt tight. I took a quick look at the faces of the other blokes in the tank with me. My new mates, Tank

Crew 247. Sitting next to me was our machine-gunner, George Hoskins. He was the same age as me, although he'd been out here for three months already, so he was battle-hardened. And he looked tough. I guessed back in Civvy Street George must have been a boxer, or else he'd got caught up in lots of street fights, because he had old scars over his eyes and his nose had definitely been broken at some point.

Up in the turret, working the huge main gun of the tank, was Harry Atkins. Harry was older than the rest of us, about thirty years old. He was over six feet, with enormous shoulders on him and built like an ox. It was his job to load the shells into the breech of the long-barrelled gun, aim, then fire.

The fifth member of our crew was our tank commander, Lieutenant Weston. Weston was twenty-three years old. He had one of those thin moustaches which a lot of the younger officers grow to make themselves look older, especially when they're commanding soldiers older than themselves.

Weston seemed all right, although I'd only met him yesterday. Harry, George and Prof seemed to respect him, so that was fine with me.

Outside, the shrill blasts of the warning whistles continued, and there were crashes as the German bombs and shells hit our position with an ear-splitting roar, WHUMP WHUMP WHUMP!

Another massive explosion. The Stukas had hit another oil dump.

German tanks were already on the horizon as I eased the Crusader forwards on its heavy caterpillar tracks. The other tanks in line were also moving up to confront the enemy.

Weston, standing above me in the turret, watched the Germans through his field glasses. They were coming at us from all directions, straight ahead, left and right flank, trying to catch us in a pincer movement.

"Half left, driver!" barked Weston. "Ready, gunner!"

While Harry loaded a shell into the breech, I sweated as I pulled on the left-hand steering lever, dragging the Crusader round to half left, and then set it rolling forwards. This was my first time driving a tank in the desert, and it was much harder than I'd expected. Back in England I'd driven tanks over roads and over mud and I'd got the hang of it. Driving a tank on sand was completely different. You'd be moving forwards over hard firm sand, and then suddenly you'd hit a soft patch and the tank, all twenty tons of it, would sink, and sand was much harder than mud to get a grip on.

Another twenty of our tanks were with us, heading towards the left flank.

All told, there must have been a hundred enemy tanks, German Panzers by the look of them, though it was hard to tell at this distance.

"Pick your target, Atkins," said Weston.

"Picked, sir," answered Harry after a few seconds. "The nearest of their tanks I can get is in my sights now."

"OK. Fire!" said Weston.

The recoil from the gun jerked us back as if we'd been kicked by a giant boot.

I looked through the periscope. Our shell had fallen short. Not that it was easy to tell whose shell was whose, as all the other tanks in our unit were now up alongside us, firing shells at the enemy as fast as they could. Meanwhile, the Germans responded with a volley of shells. One exploded about 200 yards in front of us, showering us with sand, which poured in through the hatch. Weston swiftly dropped down into the hull and pulled the hatch cover shut before we filled up with sand and choked to death.

"What can you see, Smith?" he asked.

I almost said "sand", but Weston might have thought I was being sarky. The truth was, sand *was* all I could see: the explosion had packed it against the mirror at the top of the periscope.

"Obscured vision, sir," I replied.

"Then do something about it!" snapped Weston.

I jammed on the brake and let it off again. As I'd hoped, this jolt made the sand drop away from the top of the periscope.

"Range to enemy closing," I said.

"Distance?" asked Weston.

Harry spoke up. He'd been working out the range through his porthole. "One and a half miles, sir."

"Loaded?" asked Weston.

"All ready, sir," said Harry.

"Then fire!" Weston shouted.

Once again the whole tank shook with the massive recoil. This time we got one: a Panzer directly ahead of us blew up. First, the turret sprang away from the tank like a head knocked off a doll, and then thick black oily smoke belched into the air from its engine. Finally, there was a big explosion as the fuel tank went up.

"Hit!" yelled Harry triumphantly. "One down!"

We all cheered. George let off a short burst from his machine gun and Prof gave Harry a thumbs up. I had my hands full with the levers, trying to keep us out of harm's way, but I could feel a big grin of triumph sweep across my face. At that great moment even the heat and the flies didn't seem to matter. My first piece of action and we'd scored a hit.

Meanwhile the battle raged around us. Static buzzed from the radio, and then we could hear a voice crackling in Prof's headphones, although we couldn't make out what was being said. Out of the corner of my eye I saw Prof fiddling with the radio controls, trying to get a better reception, and then we could hear the message coming through.

"More German tanks on our right, sir! Approaching from the west," Prof reported.

I sensed Weston pausing to think. "Hard right, driver! Then half left. Keep it on the turn. Zigzag course, zigzag course."

I guessed what Weston was up to: he was trying to turn us into the advancing tanks from the right so that we presented a smaller target to them. Then we'd turn again so we'd present our front to the tanks currently ahead of us. I'd done this in training. Keep moving this way and that, making a harder target to hit. Easy to do in a car, but not so easy to do in a long-based tank weighing twenty tons. Whatever we did, because of the way the Germans had come in, we'd present our long side – our vulnerable side – to one lot or the other.

I pulled the Crusader round to our right, fighting the dragging sand all the way. The controls were stiff to the touch. Maybe it was because I wasn't properly used to them. Most of the time in training we'd been driving older tanks, ones that weren't wanted so much in action. In fact, the nearest tank I'd driven to this Crusader had been a Mark III, and although the controls of both tanks were similar, they were also different enough to make driving this one difficult. Especially first time out.

Above me, Harry kept his gun aimed at the nearest advancing German tanks now on our left, the ones with the best chance of hitting us.

Luckily for us, visibility was getting bad. The light had faded as the desert sun began its final descent behind the sand dunes. Explosions and wind whipped sand into the air.

Suddenly the tank shuddered to a halt.

"What's happened, driver?" demanded Weston.

"I don't know, sir," I said. "I think some sand must have got into the gearbox, it's grinding and screaming but it won't engage."

"Hurry it up!" grated George next to me. "We're a sitting target here!"

I could feel myself sweating more as I tried to get the Crusader to move, but something had come apart. I could feel the gearbox fighting, feel it kicking through the control levers in my hands. Suddenly we lurched forwards, and Prof cheered, "Yes! The boy's done it! Well done, John!"

Then we crunched to a halt again and the gears screamed, metal against sand.

"Move it, Smith!" shouted Weston.

"I'm trying, sir!" I called back.

Outside, the air was thick with the noise of explosions, which were amplified and echoed around us inside our sweat-filled metal box.

I stamped on the clutch, threw the gearbox into neutral, then quickly flicked it into first gear. I felt the engine suddenly bite and the Crusader gave another lurch forwards before it sank down again. The gears whined as the cogs spun against metal and sand.

And then it happened.

WHUMMMPPP! It was like being struck by a giant hammer. The enemy shell must have hit our tracks. As I looked through my periscope I saw a piece of broken caterpillar track slice towards me. Then the periscope went black.

The side of the Crusader was completely stoved in, trapping Prof. Blood poured down his face from a shrapnel wound, though where exactly he was hit it was difficult to see. Harry pulled at George, dragging him out from behind his machine gun; it looked to me like he was out cold.

The smell of petrol suddenly filled my nostrils, mixing with the burning smell coming from Prof's position. The fuel tank! If that went up we'd all be cooked. It was every tank man's nightmare, being trapped inside a burning tank with no way out.

I clawed my way over to Prof and set to work untangling him from the wreckage of the radio, chucking things aside – radio parts, twisted bits of wire – not noticing that my hands were being burnt by the scorched metal.

"Up here!" yelled Weston's voice above me from the open hatch. I could see him and Harry leaning in through the turret. I pushed the unconscious Prof up, and then Harry's powerful arms came down, wrapped themselves around Prof's chest and heaved him upwards.

The smell of burning fuel was overpowering now as the inside of the tank filled with thick black choking smoke.

"Come on, Smith! Get out!" yelled Weston.

I stumbled and cracked my head on the inside of the tank as I struggled to find the hatch opening. The smoke began to engulf me. I could feel my lungs starting to fill with fumes. I couldn't breathe. I didn't know which way was up… Then a hand gripped my collar and I felt myself being lifted out.

I didn't realize it but the Crusader had been blown half on its side. I tumbled down from the burning metal on to the sand below. The air was still filled with the deafening sounds of battle, the dark night sky lip up with streaks of tracer bullets, and the atmosphere heavy with the thud-thud-thud of tank and anti-tank weapons battling it out.

The sleeves of my uniform smouldered from where I had dragged Prof from the burning metal. I dropped to my knees and poured handfuls of sand over my smoking sleeves to put them out. My hands and forearms were black, though whether from smoke or oil, or whether they were burnt, I didn't know. I could hardly feel them, which wasn't a good sign.

"Come on, let's get out of here!" yelled Harry, and he started to pull me away from the tank. My knees dragged against the sand, tearing off more skin. Then the whole desert around me suddenly exploded. I flew through the air. WHUMP! For a split second there was silence, followed by a terrible pain in my head and then … nothing.

Wounded

There was a grey film over my eyes. Smoke? No, not smoke. Something else. I didn't know where I was. My eyelids felt sticky. I was having difficulty opening them. My head thumped with a dull ache.

There was a buzzing sound. A bell? No, a fly, settling on my face.

I tried to brush it off with my hands but they felt heavy and clumsy.

A voice called: "This one's awake!"

This time I managed to open my eyes and looked around. I was in a field hospital. My hands and arms were bandaged. A medical officer stood over me. He studied me for a second or two, and then held up two fingers.

"How many fingers can you see?" he asked.

What a strange question! I thought.

"Two," I said.

"Good." The MO nodded, putting his hand down. "After that knock on the head we thought you might have double vision." He bent down to examine my head, and then I became aware of the thick bandages wrapped round it like a helmet.

"You were lucky," he commented. "You obviously have a very thick skull."

Daylight filtered into the huge tent. It was very hot. The flies were everywhere, despite the mosquito nets. Another one of them began crawling over my face and again I tried to swat it away, but it was impossible, strapped up as I was like an Egyptian mummy.

As I lay there it gradually came back to me what had happened.

"Are the others OK?" I asked.

"They'll live to fight another day," said the MO. "So will you."

There was a shout from another part of the tent, an orderly calling for him to come and take a look at a patient.

"Coming!" replied the MO. To me he said: "Don't worry, we'll soon have you back in action again." With that he went.

My head still ached. I felt awful. I felt responsible.

"How you feeling, John?" said a familiar voice.

I forced my head round and saw that Prof was lying on the next bed, with a leg bandaged up. He grinned.

"Thanks, mate," he said. "You saved my life."

"It was my fault in the first place," I said miserably. "If I hadn't stalled the tank...

"Don't blame yourself," said Prof. "Those tanks are always breaking down."

Despite what Prof said I still felt guilty. My first outing into battle and I'd messed it up. Worse, because of me, Prof was lying injured in the hospital tent.

"How are the others?" I asked.

"They're all OK," Prof assured me. "George got a bang on the head, but he's all right now. You and I are the only ones from our crew who ended up here."

"Shut up talking, you two!" snapped the orderly. "There're sick people here trying to get some sleep!"

Prof winked at me. "It's a great life in the army, innit?" he grinned.

I did my best to smile.

Next day I was able to get up, though my hands, arms and head were still heavily bandaged. Prof had to stay in bed – his ankle had been badly twisted, though nothing broken, luckily for him.

In the afternoon, Lieutenant Weston called in to see how we were. I could hardly look him in the face, I felt so guilty about stalling the tank and getting us blown up.

"I'm sorry, sir," I said.

"Sorry for getting injured?" asked Weston.

"For stalling the tank, sir," I said.

"It wasn't your fault, Smith," said Weston. "The engineers had a look at it, what's left of it. It was the gearbox. Sand had got in and clogged it up so it couldn't engage properly. The best driver in the world wouldn't have made that tank move."

That made it a bit better, but I still felt bad about what had happened.

"The other lads think you're a bit of a hero, saving Read like that. And on your first engagement, as well. Well done, Smith. We're proud to have you on our crew."

That was as maybe, but I'd been the driver and we'd been hit because the engine had stalled.

After Weston had gone, I sat by Prof's bed and we played draughts. Whether it was because I had difficulty moving my pieces with bandaged hands, or whether it was just that Prof was a better player, he beat me eight games to one. As we played we talked, and I learnt more about the rest of Crew 247.

Our huge, strong gunner, Harry Atkins, had been a blast furnace stoker at a steel mill in the north of England – a place called Consett. That explained the scars on his forearms. According to Prof, everyone who works in a steel mill has scars from bits of molten metal splashing as it's poured into the moulds.

I'd been right about George Hoskins having been a boxer. According to Prof, when he'd been called up George had been the Amateur Middleweight Champion of

North London, with the prospect of going all the way as a professional. Prof also had a high regard for Weston.

"He won't shy away from a fight, but he won't take stupid chances," said Prof. "There are too many good men who've died out here in the desert because their tank commander was after a little bit more glory than the others and did something crazy, like charging after the enemy on his own. Not that Weston won't go after the enemy, but he'll use common sense with it."

I learnt a little about Prof, too. He was in his early twenties. Back in Civvy Street he'd worked in a library, which was how he'd read so many books, and seemed to know everything. Electronics was his hobby.

"I used to build radio sets at home," he told me. "So when the time came to join up and I told the army, they put me in communications."

"You had a better recruiting officer than I did." I grinned. "I wanted to get into something with motorbikes. A messenger or something, rushing urgent messages around from general to general and to HQ and back again, tearing around on a Triumph with my leather cap and goggles on. It was what I did back home."

"What, motorbike racing?" asked Prof, impressed.

"Well, not professionally," I admitted. "In my spare time. Speedway. Cinder tracks. For work I'm an apprentice mechanic. I fix cars and bikes in my Uncle Eric's garage, but what I really want to do is race motorbikes. That's what I'd told the recruiting officer when I signed on."

"And so they put you in tanks!" grinned Prof.

"Right," I laughed. "A speed racer driving twenty tons of metal around at fourteen miles an hour. It was his idea of a joke, I suppose."

Things were quiet at the field hospital for the next week. Prof's ankle improved enough for him to be able to walk around, at first on crutches, and after that with just a bit of a limp.

Me, basically I felt OK, though my arms and hands itched so much I wanted to tear the bandages off and scratch myself to death. The skin healing, I suppose, knitting itself together. Most of us in the field hospital were all right really; all the bad cases had been taken back to Cairo for treatment, where they had proper hospital equipment. The really bad cases – where they'd lost a leg or something – were bandaged up and shipped back home to Blighty. For them the war was over.

Word came back to us through one of the medical orderlies about what was happening at the front. Apparently our boys were still holding Rommel and his Afrika Korps at El Alamein, with neither side gaining any ground from the other.

This orderly told us that Auchinleck had been removed

from his command and a new overall commander, General Alexander, was overseeing the whole Middle East operation. And some general called Montgomery had been put in charge of the Eighth Army.

"I thought General Gott was going to take over the Eighth," said Prof. "At least, that's what everyone was saying."

"He was, but the plane Gott was in was shot down a couple of days ago and he was killed, so now they're bringing out this Montgomery from England," said the orderly. He sighed. "Another general. The way this war's going we'll get through a dozen more of them before it's over."

I had to agree – it wasn't looking too clever.

Monty

Prof and I spent the next two weeks in hospital. Back at the front the battle raged, with many casualties and neither side getting anywhere. Lieutenant Weston came over once to let us know that Tank Crew 247 had been given a captured Italian tank to use until the proper replacement tanks arrived. Things went on much the same, day after day. Then, about the middle of August, panic hit the hospital, with doctors, nurses and orderlies rushing around packing things away: instruments, loose mosquito nets, anything that wasn't fixed down.

"What's going on?" I asked an orderly. "Are we retreating?"

"Monty's coming," snapped the orderly, and then rushed off.

I looked across at Prof.

"Monty?" I asked, puzzled.

"General Montgomery," said Prof. "He's obviously arrived sooner than people thought."

"Inspecting a field hospital?" I frowned. "Why?"

"From what I've heard about Monty he's that sort of general," said Prof. "He's a soldier's soldier. He likes to know what all his men think. Also, he wants to let them know that he's there to fight with them, not from some base far away from the action."

About two hours later the man himself arrived. Those of us who could walk were ordered to stand beside our beds. There was a grinding of brakes outside the tent and the sound of boots crunching on the sand as the guards on duty stamped to attention. We heard the sounds of voices outside our tent welcoming the new commander, and then suddenly he was there among us: Monty himself, Lieutenant General Bernard Montgomery, commander of the whole Eighth Army. He was shortish with a thin pointed face and a tiny moustache. What I particularly noticed was the black beret he wore on his head. It was a tank commander's beret, with the Royal Tank Regiment badge. The new commander was a tank man, one of us.

Monty did a quick tour of inspection, moving swiftly from bed to bed, asking a question now and then of the doctors, saying a few words of encouragement to some of the men who were still in bed.

When he got to me he stopped, looked up at me and read my name tags.

"Smith," he said.

"Yes, sir," I said, still standing stiffly to attention.

"I hear you performed a heroic act, Smith," he said. "Pulling a fellow crew member from a burning tank. That was a very brave act. This army could do with more men like you. Well done."

I was stunned. Speechless. Here was the commander of the whole Eighth Army, just arrived out here in Africa, and complimenting me – an ordinary private – on getting Prof out of the tank. From the urgent expression on the face of the medical officer standing just behind Monty, I realized that I was expected to say something in reply. Not knowing what else to do, I saluted with my bandaged hand and said: "Thank you, sir. I'm proud to be in the Eighth Army." Then I wished I'd said something more original.

"Good man," said Monty.

With that he moved on to the man in the next bed.

I still felt stunned. Prof, also standing to attention as best as he could on crutches, gave me a quick grin.

After his inspection, Monty went to the door of the hospital tent, then turned and addressed us all.

"Men!" he said. "It is a privilege for me to be here with you in the desert. I come here with express orders from the prime minister himself, Winston Churchill. These orders are very simple. We are to push Rommel and his forces out of North Africa. There will be no more retreats by the Allied forces. Very shortly we are going to advance from Alamein. Once we begin, there will be no turning back. We are going to fight and we are going to win. The people back home are depending on us. I will not let you down. I know you will not let the people back home down."

With that, Montgomery left the hospital tent, heading off on the next part of his whistle-stop tour of inspection of the Allied lines.

After Montgomery had gone, Prof came over to me, grinning broadly now.

"So," he said, "Crew 247 has its own hero."

"Shut up," I said, feeling embarrassed. "I don't feel like one – just the opposite. Anyway, it wasn't just me. Weston and Harry pulled you out as well."

"Yeah, but you've got the injuries," said Prof. "That makes you a hero." He turned and looked out through the tent flap at Monty's car as it sped off across the desert, leaving a cloud of sand in its wake.

"D'you think he means it?" I asked. "About us not retreating any more?"

Prof nodded. "I think he does," he said. "From now on it's going to be fight, or die fighting. Dig in and fight. Whatever, it looks like Alamein's going to be where it all happens."

Return to the Front

A couple of days after Monty's visit, the MO told me and Prof that we were being discharged and returned to the front. This was fine as far as we were concerned. We both felt frauds sitting here in the hospital when our wounds were nearly healed.

We grabbed a ride back to our regiment on a truck that was taking a load of other blokes back to El Alamein. Most of them were returning to the front after four days' leave in Cairo.

We got back to the new base camp, and then Prof and I set off to find Tank Crew 247. Our unit had taken up a position on the ridge, on the front line at El Alamein. From the state of the tanks, our forces had taken a hammering in the last few weeks: busted caterpillar tracks, scorched and dented armour all over the place.

We found Lieutenant Weston first. We stood smartly to attention in front of him and saluted.

"Driver Smith and Radio Operator Read reporting for duty, sir!"

Weston grinned. "At ease," he said. "Good to have you both back. How are the arms, Smith? And you, Read? How's the leg?"

We assured him that we were both fit enough to return to duty.

"Good," he said, "because we've got the new tank. It arrived yesterday. A Grant. Think you can handle it?"

A Grant! This was great news! The Grant was the Medium Tank M3, American-made. I'd heard about it but never actually seen one. There were two sorts of M3 tank: the Lee, which was the standard version, and the Grant, which had been made to British specifications. Although the Grant wasn't that much different from the Crusader, the two things in its favour were its heavier armour and, for me as the driver, the fact that it was reckoned to have much better manoeuvrability.

The Grant had a crew of six, compared to the Crusader's five-man crew. I wondered who our extra man was? We found out when we followed Weston to the tank lines. George and Harry were at work, making their own modifications to the Grant. With them was a young lad.

"Smith and Read, meet Private White, our new crew member," said Weston. "He's our machine-gunner and co-driver. He used to be with Crew 533 until they lost their tank and most of their crew."

I gave White a sympathetic look.

"Tough luck," I said.

"It wasn't too clever," he replied. "Only one of us was

killed. The others were wounded. I was lucky, I suppose. I came out with just a scratch on my arm."

Weston looked at his watch. "Right," he said. "There's a briefing for all tank commanders. I'll report back the top brass's intentions as soon as we've finished. In the meantime, carry on getting her into shape. You'd better take her for a spin, Smith, to get used to the controls."

With that Weston went, heading for the command tent.

"Welcome back," grinned George. "Ready for some action after all that rest?"

While we worked to get the Grant ready, Prof and I learnt a bit more about our new crew member.

Fred White was seventeen. Like nearly everyone else named White in the army, he was known as Chalky, but he didn't mind. He seemed a nice enough young bloke, tall and thin, with his black hair almost shaved to the roots. Army barbers often did that to new recruits. They said it stopped you getting lice out in the tropics, but I reckon they just enjoyed cutting everyone's hair off. Chalky came from Birmingham and had worked in a munitions factory up there, so he already knew a bit about weapons before he joined up, He'd been out here for two months as a co-driver and machine-gunner before his tank had been blown up. Although he was a quiet lad, a bit shy, once you got him talking about weapons he could go on for ever about them. A bit like me and engines and Prof and radios, I suppose. We all talk a lot about the things we're most interested in.

Because the Grant had a crew of six, there'd been some changing round of jobs to fit Chalky in. Harry would continue to load the main gun, but George would now actually aim and fire it. This way, with both of them working together, we'd get a faster rate of fire. That was another advantage of the Grant over the Crusader.

Prof and I walked around the new tank, inspecting it, while George, Harry and Chalky told us all the good points about it.

"Twenty-six miles an hour on a good surface," said Harry. "It can go up a sixty-degree gradient, and clear any obstacle two feet high. It can cross a trench six feet wide."

"What's the armour like?" I asked.

"Riveted steel, up to two inches thick in parts," replied George. "Great protection!" Again, a bit thicker than the armour on the Crusader.

"Tell them about the armaments, Chalky," said Harry. He grinned at us. "Chalky's a whizz on guns. Nearly as clever as Prof on anything technical."

Chalky patted the hull of the tank, like he was proud of it.

"The main gun in the right-hand hull is a 75 mm, with gyro-stabilizing elevation."

"In other words, you can fire it on the move," added George. "Greater control."

Chalky indicated the machine guns poking out.

"In the front is a 37 mm M5 1/50 with 178 rounds. Plus a Browning M11919A4 machine gun, with another two in the bow and one AA."

Not bad, I thought.

"The turret's hydraulically operated and can turn a full circle," put in Harry. "We can swing the turret round faster, and right round if we need to. All in all, we can fire faster and we can move faster."

"And we're calling her Bessie," said George proudly.

Harry, George and Chalky walked us round to the front where, in white letters, George had painted the name "Bessie" on her. She was the top of the range. The best. And she was ours.

Prof and I jumped up on the hull. Then I clambered down into the driver's compartment while Prof climbed up to the turret and slipped down through the hatch, into the radio operator's seat.

That was the first difference with the Grant: the driver and co-driver sat at the front of the tank in a separate compartment from the rest of the crew. Chalky and I would be communicating with Weston, and the rest of the crew in the main compartment, through headphones and throat microphones.

As I sat, I ran my hands over the steering levers, checking them for ease of movement.

There was no doubt about it, Bessie was a beauty. The Grant had obviously been built by people who knew what a tank had to do, and how difficult some of the earlier tanks had been to operate.

George leapt up beside me.

"Remember what Weston said, take her for a run," he said. "See how she works out." He grinned at me. "After all, he'd rather you knew what you were doing with her before you go into battle, than get something wrong in the middle of it."

Although I knew he was only joking, I didn't smile back. Weston and Prof had said that the tank stalling wasn't my fault, but I still didn't feel happy about what had happened. I didn't want anything going wrong next time. I needed to feel confident on my handling of the tank I was driving, especially with a brand-new one like the Grant. Like Weston said, I had to test it out. It's the same with anything that moves: it may look absolutely perfect, but the only real test of a vehicle is to drive it.

I nodded at George. Then I called to Prof, "Are you OK in the back, there? I'm going to put her through her paces."

Prof's reply came to me through the headphones, but I couldn't hear him properly. I'd forgotten about the intercom.

I picked up the headphones and throat microphone set and put them on.

"Smith to Read, come in," I said.

"Hearing you loud and clear," came Prof's voice. "No need to shout any more, John. This is a great system. Not only are we connected with base camp, but we've got intercoms. Great stuff!"

"D'you fancy going for a ride?" I asked him.

"OK by me," said Prof. "I can check the set for vibrations when mobile. Let her go."

George dropped down from the hull and I started Bessie up. The engine was noisy, but not as noisy as some tanks. I set it moving forwards, nice and slow. When you're first getting used to a new tank you don't want to go too fast.

I pulled back on my right-hand lever and turned Bessie right, out of the line, and moved her along behind the row of tanks in front of us. She turned beautifully. Mind, the sand was firm and level. I wondered how she'd cope with soggy sand.

"Smith to Read," I said into my microphone. "How you doing, Prof? Over."

"Read to Smith," came Prof's voice in my ears. "Stabilizers working perfectly. All systems operational."

I put Bessie through her paces for about half an hour, checking visibility, how she manoeuvred, lever actions, foot-pedal stiffness – all the sort of things you need to feel confident with before you take a tank into battle. Visibility was better because vision was direct: a window in a hatch in front of you. The hatch could even be opened for improved vision.

I took her out on to the open desert, although still inside our defence barriers, and brought her up to speed. Then I tried a few skid-turns, first to the left, then to the right, each time easing back on the lever and guiding her into the line of the skid. It's the sort of thing you can only do on firm sand, or gravel, or a greasy surface. Try it on soft sand and one side of the tank sinks down and you get stuck.

Bessie responded well to everything. She was a good tank. I brought her back to our place in the line and climbed down, just as Weston appeared.

"I hope you've been careful with that tank, Smith," he said with a grin. "We're going to need it."

We all looked at him inquisitively.

"We've just been given our orders," he announced. "We're going on the offensive."

Preparing for Action

We all thought that meant we were going into battle straight away, but that wasn't to be the case. Weston briefed us on Monty's long-range attack plan.

"He wants Rommel's forces weakened before we launch our next big attack," continued Weston. "Apparently Rommel's weak spot is his supply line. Because the Axis forces have pushed forward at such a speed, their front-line troops are a long way from their depots. Monty reckons that Rommel needs a quick victory because his stocks of fuel and ammunition must be running low. It takes a long time for his supplies to arrive over the distance his trucks have to travel across the desert. So, the longer we can hold out here at Alamein, the better it is for us.

"The plan is to keep the Germans at bay while the RAF mount bombing raids on the truck convoys. Obviously, some of their supplies will get through, but by the time our big push comes, Monty reckons the German forces will be low on ammunition and fuel.

"So, our orders are to sit tight, keep the enemy busy, keep alert, and be ready for the big one when it comes."

And so we waited. For two months a series of battles raged around our positions at El Alamein and the ridge at Alam el Halfa: up to the end of August, right through September and into October. At the beginning of September, Rommel's tanks launched a huge attack against our lines at Alam el Halfa, but the Eighth Army defended so fiercely that the Axis forces had to retreat. Then, early in September, while still at Alam el Halfa our New Zealand Division launched a counter-attack. This time the Axis forces defended strongly, and our boys were forced to retreat. That was the way it went for the whole of those two months: attack and counter-attack, again and again and again.

Then, on 23 October, came the orders for the big assault. Our Tank Crew 247 got our orders from Weston.

"This is it, men," he told us. "We're going forward. The long-range artillery are going to open with a barrage on the enemy positions at 2140 hours. At the same time, four divisions of infantry will start moving forward, using the barrage as our cover: The 1st South Africans, 2nd New Zealand, 9th Australian, and the 51st Highlanders. The sappers will clear a path through the minefields so our tanks can get through. It's reckoned it'll take them some time. After all, they've got to get through the barbed wire, find and clear the mines, and then mark a tank path for us. The estimated time for our tanks to start moving is 0200 hours."

Weston checked his watch.

"Right, it's now 1600 hours. I'll see you all back here at 2100 hours so we can make final preparations. In the meantime, I suggest you all get some rest. It's going to be a long night, chaps."

With that Weston left, heading for his tent.

"We've got five hours," said Harry. "I'm going to get some kip. Anyone else?"

George, Prof, Chalky and I shook our heads.

"I don't see how you can sleep at a time like this!" I said. "We're about to go into battle!"

"I can sleep because I'm older than you lot," said Harry. "I've seen it all before. And I need my rest. See you later." And with that off Harry went.

"I'm going to the mess – get something to eat," said George. "Anyone coming with me?"

"I will," said Prof. "Fancy a cuppa or something, John? Chalky?"

Chalky shook his head. He looked even paler than before. I guess he was remembering the last time he went into battle – when he'd only just made it through. I guessed he was wondering if he'd be so lucky this time.

"No," he muttered. "I think I'll just check the guns over."

"Much better to come to the mess tent," said Prof.

"I just don't feel hungry," said Chalky.

"Nor do I," said Prof. "But it's better to relax. Have a cup of tea and talk. Anyway, I'm hungry."

"Come on," I said, and I slapped Chalky on the shoulder. "Let's go and relax."

The mess tent was full, mostly with tank crews making sure they got a meal before the action started. Once the action began you never knew when you'd next get a chance to eat.

Everyone knew someone who'd been killed in this war, and so everyone was aware that for them this could be their last few hours.

"At least we're protected," said Prof. "I mean, we've got armour around us. The ones I feel sorry for are the infantry. Just blokes out there with a gun and a bayonet and a tin hat."

"Each to his own," said George. "Me, I wouldn't like to be up in a plane. At least if we get hit we can jump out of the tank. If a plane gets hit the pilot hasn't got much chance."

"They've got parachutes," pointed out Prof. "They can bail out."

"And land right on the enemy," laughed George. "Or in a tree. Or in a river. No, you've got no proper control with a parachute."

"My dad didn't want me to join up," said Chalky suddenly. "He fought in the First War. He said seeing what he saw put him off fighting for life. We had a row when I first told him I was joining up."

"That's understandable," I said.

"My mum was on my side, though," added Chalky.

He fell silent, obviously thinking about home. About his dad, and his mum.

"What's it like where you live?" I asked. I could tell he needed to talk.

"It's all right," he said. "It's all factories. That's what Birmingham is: factories, and rows and rows of houses. I had a letter from my mum just before I came out. All our streets were being bombed. It was terrible. They had to spend loads of nights in the air-raid shelters. She reckoned it was because our house is so close to the factories."

"Same thing for me," said George. "My mum wrote and said she'd spent more time down the air-raid shelters than she did at home. She's also worried about my Uncle Eric's pigeons."

"His pigeons?" asked Prof.

George nodded. "He keeps racing pigeons," he said. "On his roof." He laughed. "I ask you, all this bombing going on, people and houses getting blown up, and my mum's worried about a load of pigeons!"

"My mum cooks pigeons," said Chalky. "She makes them into pies. She said meat's hard to get hold of, so she gets my little brother to catch what he can and she turns it into stews and pies. Pigeons. Rabbits."

"I bet anyone who's got a cat or dog in your street keeps it indoors when your little brother's about," laughed George.

We all joined in laughing, thinking of Chalky's mum making pies out of people's pets.

And so it went on, just talking to pass the time, filling in the silences. I could tell that it helped Chalky to hear us talk and find out that we were all as nervous as him.

We whiled the next few hours that way, and at nine o'clock, 2100 hours, we went back to Bessie, our new Grant. Weston was already there. Harry joined us soon after, looking refreshed from his sleep. Many of the other crews had also arrived early to carry out last-minute checks on their vehicles. We checked everything twice, then a third and final time: the caterpillar tracks, the guns, the ammunition, the radio, the steering, the hatch-opening mechanism, every last nut and bolt. By the time the whistle went to assemble, every other crew was there, all ready and waiting, standing by their tanks.

I looked at my watch. 2139. One minute to go. Although we weren't due to get involved in any action ourselves until 0200, we knew once the barrage started, we were committed.

2139 and 50 seconds. 53 seconds. 54. 55. 56. 57. 58. 59.

As my watch showed 2140 hours, the barrage from our

big guns just behind us started up, a crescendo of noise as we heard WHOOOMP WHOOOMP WHOOOMP as shell after shell was sent on its way to the distant enemy positions, the sand vibrating beneath us. We could feel the shock waves even through our armour plating. This was it.

Attack!

The barrage continued as 1,000 big guns hammered and pounded the enemy positions incessantly, the shells soaring WHOOMP WHOOMP WHOOMP over our heads. The area ahead of us was now blazing with light from the bursting shells. Every now and then one of the explosions of white light would be accompanied by a flare of red flame and smoke, as a shell struck a target, though at this distance it was impossible to see clearly what had been hit.

Ahead in the distance, through the smoke, I saw the infantry come out from the slit trenches in our defensive box, and then go forward. I felt so proud to be on the same side as those blokes. Going out against enemy artillery and tanks armed only with a rifle and bayonet, and wearing a steel helmet, cardigan and shorts. We were protected inside our tank. Out there they had no protection. And the job they had to do was even more dangerous.

The sappers' job was to clear the mines along pathways – bridgeheads – through the enemy minefield, wide enough for a tank to pass safely along it. They did this by poking their bayonets into the sand, and when they found a mine they had to dig it up and put it to one side. As they cleared they marked the safe area with tape on both sides of the continuing pathway. If they trod on a mine they'd be killed or seriously maimed. As if that wasn't enough, they had to struggle to clear the barbed wire the enemy had erected as defences.

In pitch-black conditions such a job would have been certain suicide, so it needed a night like this, almost a full moon, giving enough light for the sappers to see ahead of them as they searched for mines. The trouble was, if it was light enough for them to see, they could also be seen by the enemy. That was one reason why the barrage was being laid down, to keep the enemy down, and to provide smoke for our boys.

At certain points, searchlights directed their beams straight up into the sky to help the infantry stay in the right direction; light anti-aircraft guns also fired tracer shells at intervals on fixed lines to show them the way forward.

The barrage continued relentlessly, and for the next hour the night desert pounded with heavy fire and lit up with light and gunfire. The infantry were out of sight from us now, disappeared into the smoke. More time passed. We couldn't see what was going on; all we could do was listen, and wait. Midnight came and went. Then one o'clock. Finally, after what seemed like a whole night of waiting, our orders came to "Mount up!" (a leftover from the days when the only vehicles the army used were horses) and we got on board.

I settled into the driver's seat with Chalky next to me. The other four clambered down through the turret hatch into the body of the tank: Prof first, then George and Harry, and finally Lt Weston took his command position in a seat at the top of the turret.

"OK?" I asked Chalky. He nodded and forced a grin.

"You're in safe hands with our commander," I said. "Weston's a good bloke."

We put on our communication sets and heard Weston's voice coming out through the earphones testing our connections one at a time. In turn we responded through our throat mikes:

"Driver, come in."

"Reading you, sir. Over."

"Co-driver, come in."

"Reading you, sir. Over."

And so on through the rest of the crew. Then Prof patched in to base communications, responding to their question.

"Crew 247, are you receiving? Over."

"Crew 247 reading you loud and clear. Over."

And so it went on down the rest of the line, along all the other tanks: the other Grants, the Valentines, the Stuarts, the Crusaders. All the tank crews waiting. Finally, at 0200 hours, came the order: forward.

I eased Bessie into the line of tanks and we began our

course through our own defensive minefields in single file. Once we'd cleared our own positions, we carried on in single file across the two miles of no-man's land, and then into the tank-path through the enemy minefield cleared for us by the infantry.

Once we were clear of the tape markers and into enemy territory, the tank directly ahead of us began a half-turn and I followed suit. This left the way clear for the tank behind us to move ahead into my space. The tank ahead of me went wider, and I straightened up again. I nosed forward, and now we were all in a line, headed for the enemy.

"Put a round into the breech," said Weston.

"Ready, sir," came Harry's voice. There was the sound of a large shell being slipped into the breech all ready, the sound of metal on metal echoing through to Chalky and me in our front compartment. I kept Bessie rolling.

"Fire!" snapped Weston.

George fired the big gun, and from that moment we were in action. All along the line the other tanks opened fire, shell after shell. And now the enemy responded. Ahead of us there were flashes as their field guns and tanks opened fire. The desert around us began to shake as their shells hit. Out of the corner of my eye I saw a brilliant flash of light to my right and Bessie shook violently, then recovered. The Grant immediately to our right had taken a direct hit. I kept rolling forward.

"Pick up some speed, Smith," said Weston. "Put some space between us and their shells."

"Sir," I said.

I opened the throttle and increased the speed to 25 miles an hour. Weston was hoping that the field guns of the Axis forces would be calculating our speed at 15 miles an hour, dropping their shells accordingly. Although we were now getting nearer to the enemy, his theory was that we would be travelling faster than they guessed and so their shells would fall behind us. It was a good theory, provided we didn't get hit by shells falling short.

George and Harry were obviously working like clockwork together because Chalky and I could hear the slide of metal on metal as Harry loaded the shells into the breech, followed by the huge crash of the shells being fired at regular and fast intervals.

Suddenly the sky ahead of us was lit up by flares bursting bright above the Axis positions, illuminating them clear as daylight. The RAF had started their attack. Tracers of machine gun and anti-aircraft fire poured upwards into the sky from the Axis positions, trying to bring down the planes overhead. We continued pounding the enemy positions.

Over my earphones I heard Prof say: "Copy that. Over and out." He had obviously had instructions from HQ. This was confirmed when he relayed them to Weston.

"Orders from base, sir," Prof said, all of us hearing his

voice in our phones. "Take a direction due east. Panzer Division approaching."

Our planes had spotted a counter-attack coming from the German positions.

"Due east, Smith," said Weston.

"Aye, sir," I said.

I eased the right-hand lever back and swung Bessie round, checking the compass and turning until I had an easterly direction. Out of the corner of my eye I saw four other tanks doing the same. I guessed there were others joining us. We had obviously been chosen as the group to confront the oncoming Panzers.

By now it was past three o'clock in the morning. The battle had been raging for over five hours, ever since our big guns had begun their barrage. We left the rest of our tanks to continue their advance towards the Axis positions while our group headed due east across the open desert.

A double note in my earphones told me that a radio transmission was coming in. Then I heard Prof's voice responding with "Received" and "Copy" and "Over and out". We soon learned what it was all about when he relayed it to Weston and we picked up their conversation over our headsets.

"Captain Mason of Tank Crew 333 presents his compliments, sir," said Prof. "He's been detailed by HQ to take charge of this squadron."

"Tell Captain Mason we are happy to oblige," said Weston. "What are his orders?"

"Crew 333 will take point position. We are to proceed at his speed in convoy behind him until he gives the order to stop. Douse all lights. No firing. He says he doesn't want to alert the enemy to our position. He says there's a ridge about nine miles ahead which will give us cover. We will lay in an ambush for the enemy there."

"Acknowledge," said Weston.

Prof relayed Weston's message back to the radio operator of Crew 333. For the next half an hour we travelled at roughly twenty miles an hour over the desert sand. To our left and behind us the fighting continued with flares and explosions. Even at this distance from the battle, the sand vibrated and the desert echoed as the heavy guns of both sides crashed out their shells. We slid silently through the night in single file, with just the sound of the engine beating, our gear wheels clonking and grinding, and our caterpillar tracks swishing over the sand.

The radio crackled into life again, and then Prof once more relayed the instructions from Captain Mason in Tank 333: "Halt."

I eased on the brake and brought Bessie to a halt. We sat there with the engine idling.

"Captain Mason's orders," said Prof: "take up position to the right of the ridge ahead."

"To the right of the ridge ahead," acknowledged Weston.

I pulled Bessie round and headed for our new position. The tank behind me did the same, pulling up alongside me. Soon all eight tanks were in place, four at each side of the high ridge, our guns trained on the dip in the ridge where the Panzers would be expected to come through. Now all we could do was sit there and wait.

"I hate this waiting," Harry's voice grumbled through my headphones.

"You'll be in action soon enough," replied Weston smoothly.

The radio crackled again, then Prof reported to us: "Captain Mason's going out to take visual observation."

Sure enough we saw the hatch of Tank 333 open, then the figure of Captain Mason climb out and drop down. He made his way up the high ridge, crouching low all the time. When he got near the top he dropped on to his front and crawled the last few feet to the top. From my open hatch I could see him raise his binoculars to his eyes, then scan the desert ahead. On the eve of a full moon, visibility wasn't bad. Mason lay like that for a moment or two, and then he got up quickly and slid back down the ridge. He looked like a man in a hurry.

Having raced back to his tank, he dropped back down into the turret and pulled the hatch shut after him. A few seconds later we heard Prof on the radio receiving an incoming message.

Prof relayed the news to Weston, and so to the rest of us.

"Captain Mason's compliments, sir, but he says we've got a spot of bother," he announced. "He says either the RAF boys underestimated just how big the Panzer Division is that we've been sent to intercept, or the Germans decide to increase it after it was spotted."

"Give us the bad news, Read," said Weston. "How many of them are there?"

Prof hesitated, then he said: "Captain Mason estimates about fifty Panzers heading this way. They should be at the ridge in about five minutes."

We all let this sink in. Fifty Panzers against eight of us. We were outnumbered by more than six to one. Weston was silent for a moment, then he asked Prof: "Does Captain Mason have any orders as what our tactics should be?"

"Yes, sir," said Prof. "He's radioed our situation back to base. In the meantime he orders us to continue as before. He's working out a plan for a delaying action until reinforcements arrive."

It had taken us hours to get to this point from HQ. Our

nearest support tank unit was over an hour away, and they would be engaged in the big battle going on behind us.

We all fell silent as we weighed the situation up. It would be at least two hours before any reinforcements arrived, and fifty enemy tanks would be upon us in less than five minutes.

Outnumbered

New orders from Captain Mason in Tank 333 came through within the next few minutes.

"We're going to set up an ambush for the enemy. All tanks to withdraw to new positions half a mile back from the ridge, in two groups of four, leaving a gap half a mile wide between them to allow the German tanks to come through. The group on the west of the ridge will be led by Tank 333, the group to the east by Tank 247. The tank at the rear of the west group is to keep its main gun aimed at the first German tank through the gap, the tank at the rear of the east group to keep the second tank in its sights, and so on down the line. Fire on my mark. All lights to be kept extinguished throughout this manoeuvre, at least until the order is given to fire."

I turned Bessie round and our east group drove out in a spread-out line until we had reached the designated point half a mile from the ridge. Then we turned so that our guns were pointing towards the gap in the ridge, but clear of hitting the west group.

We took up our positions with just two minutes to go before the German tanks were due to appear.

"Engines off," came the orders.

I switched off the engine. Harry slid a shell into the breech of the main gun. Chalky checked the rounds about to be fed in the machine gun. I turned to Chalky and gave him a grin.

"Don't worry," I whispered. "This tank is the best there is. And, like I said, Weston is a good commander. We'll be OK."

We waited. We could hear the engines and the tracks of the Panzers clearly now. Our hope was that they would roll straight past us, at least long enough for us to gain the element of surprise. But we'd have to have a lot of luck on our side: the sky was already starting to show streaks of light. Dawn wasn't far away.

The first of the Panzers drove through the gap in the ridge. We let it continue. There was a pause, then came the second, then the third. They were assuming that if they were to be attacked it would have happened at once, as soon as the first of their tanks appeared. Mason was counting on lulling them into a sense of security, letting as many as possible get through, and then hitting them from behind.

Unfortunately for us, the commander of the sixth Panzer tank was more watchful than his comrades. He obviously spotted one of the tanks in the west group because even from the distance we were, I saw the tank turret start to swing and knew that he was getting ready to fire. Captain

Mason had obviously seen it too, because the radio crackled, and then Prof shouted the order: "Fire!"

All of our tanks opened up at once, their shells hammering into the target tanks they'd been allocated, and the night sky was suddenly filled with fire as the shells struck home, into the Panzers.

Even as our first target burst into flames, Weston had ordered George to aim the gun at the next Panzer just coming through the gap in the ridge. George fired at the same time as one of our other tanks, who obviously had the same idea. The Panzer in the gap blew up, and then sank down on to the sand, broken, with black smoke and orange flames pouring out from its shattered turret.

Seven of their tanks were now out of action, and the gap in the ridge was blocked.

"Turn to guard against the sides of the ridge!" came the order.

All our tanks swung round so that our guns were now pointed at the far ends of the ridge, the only way left for the remaining Panzers to attack us. Some of the Panzers had already begun firing blind over the ridge, but their shells flew harmlessly over our heads.

Panzer tanks began to appear at the far end of the ridge, about a mile away, their great guns swivelling towards us.

"Target and fire at will!" commanded Weston.

Over my earphones I could Harry grunting with the effort as he lifted the heavy shells and loaded, while George fired – WHOOMP WHOOMP WHOOMP – one shell after the other. The first Panzer sank down as George's shell struck, crippling it. The gun of the second Panzer was already swinging round towards us and I tensed, waiting to be hit, but the shell missed and crashed into the tank next to us.

"See what you can do, driver," came Weston's voice over my earphones.

"Will do, sir," I said.

I began to move Bessie forward, weaving to left and right all the time to avoid the Panzers getting an easy bearing on us. Fortunately, with the Grant's gyro-stabilizers, Harry and George still had control of aiming the gun, despite the movement.

Some of the Panzers were now actually coming over the top of the ridge, bearing down on us, guns blazing. There was a lot of noise coming from the radio now as messages flew back and forth between Command Tank 333 and the other tanks, but Prof wasn't bothering to relay any of the messages unless they had a direct bearing on our position and course of action. Every now and then we heard an explosion near to us, and realized that one of our own tanks had taken a hit. Through the window of my hatch I saw one of our tanks break away and begin to make a run for it, followed by another, heading back to our own lines. Neither made it. As I watched both of them took direct hits right into the back, exploding the petrol tank and pushing the engine right through into the hull. Both tanks blew up. The poor devils inside wouldn't have had a chance.

"Charge towards the enemy!" ordered Weston.

I swung Bessie towards the top of the ridge, and charged. It may have sounded a crazy thing to do, rush at the enemy, but it was a sensible decision. For one thing the most vulnerable part of a tank is the rear, where the engine and petrol tank are. For another, if you rush at an enemy, firing all the time, you hope it puts them off taking proper aim at you.

I drove on, and now beside me Chalky was firing the machine gun at the tank we were approaching. Some of the bullets bounced off the Panzer's armour plating, but some must have penetrated the vision hatch because the German tank suddenly veered wildly to one side and crashed into another Panzer.

George and Harry were still keeping up the firing, only now they'd switched to the smaller gun, the 37 mm. At this closer range it was just as effective and faster to load and fire.

It all sounds as if we were organized, but the truth is that the battle was chaotic. When this much metal is flying around at enormous speeds and you can be killed from one second to another, you just do the best you can to survive: dodging, weaving, and firing back, and doing your best to keep a clear head. But you can have the clearest head in the world and it won't do you a bit of good if the enemy hit you with a lucky or a well-aimed shot.

The noise as in all tanks battles was deafening. We had now given up trying to hear any instructions, even over the earphones. We couldn't hear a thing except the crash of guns and the sounds of explosions. Bessie rocked a couple of times as stray German shells hit us, but our armour held and the shells just bounced off to explode outside the tank.

I don't know how long we had been fighting, it seemed like hours, but I'd heard it always does, even if it's just minutes. I kept Bessie rolling backwards and forwards along the cover of the ridge while George and Harry fired their 37 mm and Chalky let fly with the machine gun. The only one of our tanks that I could see still moving was Captain Mason's 333. It wasn't too far from us, just about fifty yards away. Even as I watched it took a couple of hits. Its metal caterpillar tracks slid off like an orange being peeled, and its turret buckled. Another German shell thudded into it, and the tank flipped half over and the figure of Captain Mason fell out of the hatch, dropping to the ground like a rag doll. The captain lay there on the sand, and we could see him rolling in agony. A Panzer was heading straight for him, and at the speed it was going it didn't look like it was going to stop. Mason was about to be crushed beneath its tracks. It was then that Weston did one of the bravest things I've seen. He shouted, "Cover me!" and flipped open the hatch, clambered out of the turret and dropped down on to the sand. Then he ran towards the wounded Mason in an attempt to drag him out of the path of the oncoming Panzer. Harry and George both grabbed at the Browning machine guns, and they and Chalky opened fire at the Panzer, shooting over the crouching Weston's head, their tracers of bullets smashing into the hull and the Panzer's turret. I drove Bessie forward to where Mason lay, ready to pick Weston and Mason up. The Panzer still powered on, its huge mass towering over Mason's fallen body. Weston just got there in time. He grabbed the captain under the arms and hauled him to one side, just as the Panzer rolled past, right over the spot where Mason had been lying. I don't know why the Panzer gun crew didn't hit us with their main gun. Maybe they had problems with it. Maybe it had jammed. That happens with some guns after they've been firing non-stop. Whatever the reason, if they had opened fire they would have blasted us into nothing. As it was, George suddenly let fly with a 37 mm shell and hit them smack in the front, right in the driver's hatch.

I was trying to keep my eye on Weston and Mason down there on the sand, and positioning Bessie between them and the other Panzers.

Suddenly I saw Weston put his hands up. It was then I realized how quiet it was all of a sudden. All the tanks had stopped firing.

"They've got him," said Chalky beside me, shock and anger in his voice.

A machine gun was trained on the lonely figure of Weston. Then another. In the silence a voice called out to us in broken English across the desert night.

"Yours is the only tank left, Britishers. You cannot win now. Surrender, or we will shoot your comrade. And then we will shoot you."

"What shall we do?" asked Prof's voice in my earphones. He was talking to all of us, not just to me.

I looked out through the window of my hatch. It looked to me like we were surrounded on all sides by Panzers, all with their main guns pointed straight at us. If we resisted we'd be blasted into a mass of crumpled metal.

"You have ten seconds!" called the voice. "After that, I give the orders to fire and you will all die. Ten. Nine. Eight..."

As we listened to the German commander count down, Harry said grimly: "We haven't got a chance. At least if we give up now, maybe we can save ourselves later."

The German commander counted on.

"…Six. Five. Four…"

"Maybe if we started firing first we'd catch them by surprise?" suggested Chalky, desperation in his voice.

"And two seconds later Weston would be dead on the sand, and we'd be turned into ashes," Prof said. He sighed. "Outnumbered like we are, I don't think we've got much choice, lads."

"…Two. One."

I heard the turret hatch scrape back, then George's voice shouted out: "All right! We're coming out!"

Chalky and I hauled ourselves up and out of the driver's compartment and joined George, Harry, Prof and Weston on the sand, our hands held up over our heads. Some of the Germans came out of their tanks now and joined us on the sand, their guns trained on us. One look at their grim expressions on their faces was enough to tell us they'd shoot us if we tried anything.

I looked around at the scene. It was carnage, smoke from burning tanks drifting around us, bodies lying scattered about on the sand. Captain Mason still lay just a few feet away from us. It was pretty obvious to all of us that he was already dead. Weston looked down at him and shrugged.

"Still, at least I saved him from being run over," he said.

"Silence!" snapped a voice, and then a German officer stepped past the soldiers with their machine guns and glared at us.

"As commanding officer of this unit, I insist that we are treated as prisoners of war in accordance with regulations," demanded Weston.

"You do not need to insist," the German officer replied coldly. "The army of the Third Reich does everything by the rule book."

"Only checking," said Weston. "In that case, take us to your leader."

The way Weston said it, trying to make a joke despite the mess we were in, and all the death around us, made the rest of us want to laugh. Well, it made me, George and Harry want to laugh. Chalky and Prof both looked nervous about the whole thing.

The Germans searched us for weapons. Then they made us sit down cross-legged on the sand with our hands on our heads.

"As soon as the transport arrives you will be taken to the nearest transit camp," said the officer. "You are now prisoners of war. For all of you, the war is over."

Captured

As the sun came up fully on a new day, two armoured cars loaded with armed German soldiers, and an open truck, arrived. When they pulled up near us we had been sitting on the sand with our hands on our heads for nearly two hours. In those hours we'd had plenty of time to take in the aftermath of last night's battle. Bessie was the only tank of our original eight that had survived. All the other seven had been destroyed. As far as we could see we'd taken out almost twenty of the Panzers, which was a pretty good rate of exchange in war terms for our side, but in human terms it was a catastrophe. All those men dead.

I sat there, hands on my head, and looked at Bessie. Her hatch hung open. Her sides were scorched and scarred from shell bursts, her tracks damaged. But she'd done us proud. Her armour had resisted all that the Panzers had thrown at us; her steering had got us out of trouble during the battle; her stabilizers had kept our guns firing firmly and steadily throughout. She was a great tank. And now we were losing her.

The German tank commander handed us over to another German officer. He and his men tied our wrists with strong cord, and then they loaded us at gunpoint on to the open truck. That done, they tied our legs together so that we couldn't suddenly jump off the truck and run away while it was moving. Three of the armed soldiers then jumped into the back with us and kept their guns on us. We lay roped together and just glared at them. There wasn't a lot to say.

The lead car started up, and then we set off in convoy, one car at the front, then us in the truck, then the second car keeping watch on us.

By now the early sun was starting to get hot. The desert around us looked smooth as we travelled, leaving the scene of the battle behind us: the wreckage of twisted metal; birds circling overhead, waiting to get their pickings from the dead. Apart from the sounds of the circling birds, it was quiet, the quiet of the dawn after the battle of the night before.

We drove across the desert for about an hour, about twenty miles I guessed from the speed of the convoy over that terrain. From that, and the position of the sun, we knew that we were now well behind Axis lines.

Then we saw a camp ahead: lines of tents and vehicles, mainly lorries and jeeps. Next to this camp was a large compound surrounded by a very high wire fence. There were men inside. As we got nearer we saw that they were Allied soldiers, about a hundred of them. It was a prisoner-of-war transit camp.

"Once we get behind that wire it'll be even harder to get out," grumbled George.

"Are you suggesting we make a break for it?" whispered Harry.

"I don't think that's a good idea," I muttered. "Tied together like this, we wouldn't get five yards before we'd all be dead. At least while we're alive we've got a chance."

"Silence!" shouted one of the soldiers.

We shut up. It only took another five minutes or so before our convoy pulled up in front of the first tent in the camp. The soldiers undid the ropes from our ankles and wrists and pushed us roughly down from the back of the truck on to the sand. Once more, we lined up. The German officer in charge got down from his jeep and went up to Weston.

"It is now my duty to hand you over to the Italian army," he announced.

We shot quick looks at each other. This was bad news. We'd all heard reports from prisoners who'd escaped about how they were treated in the different prisoner-of-war camps, and the Italians were known to treat Allied prisoners badly. Whether it was revenge for the humiliation they had experienced back in 1941, when Wavell's 30,000 men had taken the whole Italian army prisoner, all 250,000 of them, we didn't know. All we did have were reports of

Italian guards beating and shooting unarmed prisoners, and sometimes leaving the wounded to suffer.

Weston caught our looks of concern. He obviously felt just as worried about our future as prisoners.

"I must remind you, as an officer, that we were taken prisoner by an officer of the German army, and as such we should remain prisoners of the German army."

"And I must tell you that we of the German army are here to fight a war, not to look after prisoners!" the officer snapped back.

By now we had been joined by a patrol of Italian soldiers, led by an officer who had more medals on his tunic than anyone I'd ever seen before, short of a general.

The enemy officers gave each other a salute before talking briefly in German.

A short time later we were marched into the compound under a guard of Italian soldiers. The main gates of the compound clanged shut behind us, and then they were locked and chained. We were now properly prisoners of war.

It didn't take us long to get settled in. A prisoner-of-war camp is run much the same as any other army camp. The most senior officer is in charge of the Camp Committee, consisting of the other officers. They give the orders out to the rest of the prisoners. They also deal with the enemy commanders on behalf of the prisoners. In the case of this particular camp, the most senior officer was a Major Benson. There were two captains and four lieutenants, including Weston. Weston's rank automatically put him on the Camp Committee.

These camps weren't actually proper prisoner-of-war camps; they were called transit camps, places to keep the prisoners until they could be moved on. Our transit camp was just a large, square, flat open area of hard and rocky sand with a tall double fence going all the way round it. There were no tents, no cover of any kind, except what the men had been able to make themselves out of their greatcoats, those that had them. Groups of men sat around talking or playing makeshift games. The mood of everyone was one of boredom and frustration. There was no privacy.

The Italians had set up machine-gun posts at each corner of the compound, the guns aimed at us. Any trouble and they could fire in through the fence and mow us down.

The prisoners were a mixed bunch, just like the rest of the army – English, Scots, Welsh, Irish, Australians, New Zealanders, Rhodesians, South Africans and Indians. We soon learnt how the prisoner-of-war routine worked.

"They take us in batches over to Italy," said Dirk, a South African private. "Once they've got enough of us, they load us on to trucks and then take us to the nearest port."

"How many's enough?" I asked.

Dirk shrugged. "A few hundred. It depends. To be honest, you never know where you are with these Italians. They're all a bit chaotic. One week they may take four lorry-loads, the next, just one lorry-load. I suppose it depends on how many they're taking from one of the other transit camps."

"How long have you been at this place?" asked Prof.

"Two weeks," said Dirk. "My guess is I'll be going on the next load. It wouldn't surprise me to find they clear us all out in one go."

The big complaint among most of the men seemed to be the lack of cover. In the daytime the sun blazed down, and at night it was cold, as is often the way in the desert. Those who had been captured with their greatcoats were the lucky ones; they had something to wrap round at night to keep warm. Some of the others had dug themselves holes in the sand to keep warm at night, though they said you didn't want to dig too deep because the further down you went, the colder the sand was. Make a bed-shelter from the top layer of sand, that's what they advised. The sun heated it up during the day and it would keep you warm for a few hours at night, at least.

The whole business of being exposed like this, the very fact of having been taken prisoner and now being herded into this compound like sheep, meant morale was very low. Most of the blokes seemed to have given up on the war and many were looking forward to being shipped over to Italy to a proper prisoner-of-war camp.

I saw Weston heading back towards us, having just finished his meeting with Major Benson. I signalled to the rest of our crew and we joined him over by the fence, a bit apart from the rest of the prisoners. He told us much the same story as Dirk had. The Italians were waiting for more lorries to arrive to take us all to the nearest port, and then on to Italy, where we'd spend the rest of the war in a camp.

"Not for me!" grunted George.

"Nor me!" I said.

Harry, Prof and Chalky nodded. We all looked at Weston.

He nodded in agreement: "We're getting out," he whispered.

Prisoners of War

We spent the rest of the day walking around the inside of the compound, circuit after circuit, in pairs. Me and Weston. George and Harry. Prof and Chalky. The Italian guards thought we were exercising and laughed at us. In reality we were checking every part of the wire fence, looking for the weak spot. We didn't find it.

In the afternoon the compound gates opened and armed Italian soldiers ordered us back, while others brought in three long wooden trestle tables. The prisoners detailed by the Camp Committee then came forwards and set the trestle tables up. That done, the Italians brought in two large steaming tureens. As the smell of the food hit me, I realized I hadn't eaten for nearly a whole day and my stomach was desperate for food. We lined up at the tables. Each of us picked up a metal spoon, and then one by one we filed past to have our plates filled up with a kind of stew. Tinned meat with some sort of pasta, by the look of it. Plus a bit of hard bread. I was so hungry I didn't care what it was.

We found ourselves a separate place on the sand, sat down and began to eat. While we ate we talked.

"Right," said Weston, "let's have some reports. The fence?"

We all shook our heads.

"The first problem is it's a double fence," said Prof. "Even if we get through the first fence, we've still got to get through the second one. And by that time the chances are the guards will have spotted us. They're not that brilliant, but they don't have to be brilliant to guard us out here in the middle of the desert."

"We can't get over the fence for the same reason," added George. "Plus, as soon as we get on the top we'd present the perfect target."

"And tunnelling under it's out as well," sighed Chalky. "If we tried to do it quickly, we'd be spotted."

"And we don't have time to tunnel out slowly because the lorries could be here any day and take us all away," nodded Weston. He didn't seem at all disturbed by what we'd just said. He'd obviously been expecting it. He looked around at us.

"Any disagreements on all those points so far?"

We all munched our bread and shook our heads.

"Then we're all agreed that we can't get out through, over or under the fence," he said. "Which leaves only one way out."

"Fly?" suggested George.

We all laughed. Then I suggested: "We wait till they come to get us in the lorries."

Weston nodded. "My thought exactly," he said. "From what everyone's said they'll take all of us. After all, there are only about a hundred of us here."

"We can't do it on our own, skipper," said Harry. "What about the rest of the blokes? We'll have to let them know."

"I know," agreed Weston. "I'll talk to the major and put it to the Camp Committee."

"A mass breakout," mused Prof.

"What do we do if the Camp Committee doesn't agree"? I asked.

"There's only one thing we can do," said Weston. "We escape on our own, without the others. Agreed?"

We looked at each other and nodded.

"Agreed," we said together.

Planning the Escape

Next morning after breakfast – if you could call the watery gruel that we were given "breakfast" – I went for a stroll around the inner fence with Prof, and we had a surprise. There, parked about a hundred yards outside the fence, in between the lorries and jeeps, was Bessie. The Germans had brought her in and the Italians were keeping her on display like a prize trophy, just to let us know they were winning this desert war.

As we looked at her, an idea struck me.

"We could use Bessie to escape," I whispered to Prof.

Prof glanced at me in surprise, then at Bessie, then back at me again. Behind his glasses his eyes looked at me as if I'd gone mad with the sun.

"Think about it," I said. "It'd be perfect." And I explained my thinking to him, very briefly, in a low voice. I didn't want anyone overhearing. It only took a few minutes of talking to him, and then Prof was nodding in agreement.

"It could work," he said thoughtfully.

"Of course it could," I said. "Let's go and see the others before Weston goes before the Camp Committee."

We hurried back to where George, Harry and Chalky were making a set of playing cards out of old Italian newspapers. Weston was just on his way to see the major to put our escape idea to him. I made sure we couldn't be overheard before telling them all that we'd seen Bessie and my idea for using her to escape.

"Escape in a tank?" asked Harry. "Are you potty? At the speed that moves, a man on a bike will be able to catch us!"

"Not with Bessie," I replied. "Twenty-six miles an hour, top speed. She's a good tank! Plus we'll be armed. Machine guns. The main gun. Get to our tank and we can blast this camp, stopping the Italians radioing for help. Shoot up their vehicles. It will give us all the time we need to get back to our own lines."

"Providing the Germans have left the ammunition in the tank," said George.

"They're bound to have," I said. "After all, they'll want to use it themselves. I bet it's only here because it's in reserve. They'll paint out our symbol and put their own on it. Anyway, I don't want to leave Bessie behind when we go. She's too good a tank to abandon like that."

"If you think about it from the communication side, it's a good idea," added Prof. "We'll have a radio. Once we get back within radio range we could contact HQ and let them know what's going on."

"Providing we don't get blown up before that," grunted Harry, still not convinced. "I reckon we'd be better off with something faster – one of those Italian lorries or a jeep with a machine gun on it."

"And getting shot at by our own side," laughed Weston. "Yes, I think John's idea is a good one. We get out, get Bessie back, and off we go. All I have to do is sell the idea to the others."

While Weston went off to talk to the Camp Committee, I took a walk to the wire fence to look at Bessie again. An Italian soldier arrived beside her carrying a tin of paint and a brush. As I suspected, he was going to paint out our British army symbols, and then repaint her with Italian colours. He didn't look like he was very keen on the job, but then most soldiers aren't keen on doing those sort of jobs. A soldier in the army can make painting anything last weeks, because he knows that once he's finished one painting job he'll just be given another, so why hurry and make more work for yourself?

The Italian soldier began painting over our symbols with very slow and careful brushstrokes, taking his time. It pained me to see our symbols being painted out like this, but I knew in my heart that we'd be getting Bessie back soon, and it didn't matter what colours she wore: she was our tank.

The Camp Committee of seven officers were in deep discussion in the centre of the compound. You may think it odd that this sort of thing could go on: officers discussing something like an escape right in plain view of everyone, but in a way that was why they could do it. Because there was no cover and everyone just sat or walked around looking listless and defeated, the guards didn't think that anyone would try anything. No one had tried to escape yet. The fences were too high. The machine guns kept everyone in their place, and quiet. The transit camp was a long way away from the actual fighting. All this made the guards just that little bit too complacent, which was good for our escape plan. If the Camp Committee agreed to it.

I turned and saw that Weston wasn't having an easy time of it. There were arguments going on among the officers, though no one was raising their voice. Every now and then Major Benson lifted a hand to quieten someone down, and then the discussion resumed.

The Italian guards watched all this from their machine-gun posts with amusement. As far as they were concerned the Camp Committee was discussing things like the quality of the food or the lack of shelter. That was what they usually talked about, and then the major would take the complaints to the camp commander. The guards weren't bothered; they were quite happy for the prisoners to squabble among themselves. Divided and unhappy prisoners were less likely to get together and cause them problems.

Finally the Camp Committee finished its session. The officers went back to their units to report. I left the fence and hurried towards our crew as Weston returned, trying to walk as casually as possible so as not to alert the guards that anything special was going on. I looked at the faces of the other officers as I walked. Some of them looked pleased, but at least two looked very unhappy. I arrived back with Harry, George, Prof and Chalky just as Weston did.

"We're go!" announced Weston triumphantly.

"All of them?" asked Harry. Like me, he'd seen the expression on the faces of those two officers.

"Most," said Weston. "The other two will back it. After all, we're in the army and orders are orders."

Talking in low tones, he outlined the plan. As Weston spoke to us, the other officers were doing the same, spreading the word around.

"When the lorries arrive to take us away, we line up and go along with it, doing nothing to put the Italians on their guard. There will be about ten Italians in charge of loading us, all armed. Once we start to get on to the lorries, two men will begin an argument, with one accusing the other of pushing him."

"Which two?" asked George.

"Two of the Australians," said Weston. "Captain Fraser of the Ninth Australian Infantry Division reckons two of his men will be delighted to do it. Their argument will turn into a fight. The guards will come over to break it up, but the fight will spread, with other soldiers joining in. For a few seconds there will be chaos, and in those few moments all the action will have to take place. The men nearest to the guards will jump them, bringing them down and taking their guns off them. Once they've got the guns they open fire on the other Italians. It will all have to be done very, very fast, before the Italians realize what's happening. We have force of numbers on our side, but they've got the weapons. During all this we take one of the guns and make for our tank. It's our job to recapture Bessie, start her up, and then cause havoc while the rest of them get back on to the lorries and make their escape. Once the lorries are on their way, we can leave. It was on that basis that I sold it to them. Everyone else goes first, we go last and give them cover with Bessie."

"Why were there some grim faces among the officers?" asked Harry.

"Because they know that it's not going to be that simple," said Weston. "The Italians will start shooting and men are going to get killed. Some of them are very close to being taken to safety after two years of hard fighting, even if it is only to a prisoner-of-war camp, and they're not happy about taking the risk of being killed."

"You mean they'd rather stay as prisoners than take the chance of getting back to their own units?" said Chalky, amazed.

"Don't blame them so quickly," replied Weston. "When you've been out here as long as some of us, and seen some of the fighting and death that we've seen, maybe you'd be just as keen for a rest."

"Has anyone any idea when the next lot of lorries are due to take us away?" I asked.

"No," said Weston. "It could be any day now. It could be weeks. All we can do … is wait."

Breakout

And so we waited. The days passed. We spent them sitting around, talking, playing games of cards with the makeshift pack that George, Harry and Chalky had made. Sometimes we played noughts and crosses in the sand. We ate twice a day beneath the hot sun: watery gruel for breakfast and a hot kind of stew in the afternoon, with hard bread. It was the same routine, every day. None of the prisoners did anything to upset this routine so the guards were kept happy. The whole atmosphere was relaxed and easy, which was exactly what we wanted it to be. We wanted the guards to feel safe and secure. That way we hoped they'd be at ease when the time came for us to get on the lorries, so they would be taken by surprise when the trouble started. We spent four days like this, just lazing around in the heat during the day, and shivering in the cold of the desert night, trying to sleep. On the fifth day we knew that something was up. There was a new tension about the guards. They started preparing three of the lorries that were parked up, and rushing around, with lots of shouting of orders. We all kept quiet, watching the goings-on through the wire fence. In the distance we could see a large dust cloud getting nearer. More lorries were on their way.

Armed soldiers appeared, who took guard at the compound entrance. The gates were opened and an Italian officer came in. His second in command stood next to him and began to shout in English.

"Attention! For you the war is over. You are very lucky. You are about to go somewhere safe. Gather all your belongings and line up."

Major Benson then took over, stepping forward and issuing exactly the same orders to line up, but without telling us how lucky we were.

We took up our possessions, what few we had, and started to form a line by the gates.

Weston made sure that he, George, Harry, Chalky and Prof were near the back of the line. I had volunteered to be the one to use the gun to help Crew 247 get to Bessie, so I positioned myself further along the line near to the two Australians who had volunteered to stage the fight. That way I would be near enough to step in and get the gun. The Australians were both big men, with big arms and tough-looking faces.

We stood at ease under the watchful eyes of the armed Italian soldiers, and waited. The lorries were getting nearer and nearer now. We all kept quiet, giving the appearance of complete listlessness. We didn't want to alert the Italians that anything might go wrong with their operation. So far there had been ten or twelve transports of prisoners from this camp, with no problems. There was no reason for them to think that this one might be different.

The three lorries from the base had been moved to just outside the gates. Four new lorries arrived. Three of them went and parked up, and the fourth joined the other waiting lorries. That made sense: they couldn't transport prisoners until they had replacement lorries, otherwise the transit camp would be left without vehicles.

The armed guards now moved into the compound and began shouting at us in Italian. Although we couldn't understand what they were saying, the way they gestured with their guns at us, at the gate and at the waiting lorries made their message clear enough.

We shuffled forwards, heads down, shoulders slumped, out through the compound's open gates, heading for the waiting lorries. The guards had relaxed, sensing there would be no trouble from us.

Twenty-five men clambered on board the first lorry and the guards relaxed just a little bit more.

The next batch of men were just starting to haul themselves up on the tailboard of the second lorry when it started. One of the Australians pushed the other out of the way, as if to get on the lorry before him. The other Australian didn't say a word, but just belted him. It was supposed to be a fake punch, but it looked real enough to me. The one who'd been hit crashed down to the ground and his attacker jumped on him. Soon the pair were rolling about in the sand, punching, grabbing, shouting and swearing. Two of the nearest guards ran over to them with their guns raised, while another couple kept the other prisoners back. Rifle butts crashed down on the arms of the fighting prisoners. Suddenly the two Australians leapt up from the ground and grabbed the guns, pulling the two guards down. Caught off balance, the Italians fell over. The other guards heard them yell out in alarm and instinctively turned to see what was going on. That was the moment everyone had been waiting for. We bundled forwards, jumping on the other guards, who shouted for help.

The remaining guards saw what was happening and started firing their weapons, but they had to shoot over the heads of the prisoners in case they hit their own men.

The fallen guards were desperately trying to hang on to their rifles, but as the punches and kicks rained down on them they had no chance. One of them had a machine gun. He let go of it to try and protect himself. I managed to snatch it up from the ground. I fired a burst into the air to let Weston and the others know that I was armed.

"Go!" Weston yelled at our crew, and we all began running towards Bessie, me keeping well to the right of Weston, Prof, Harry, George and Chalky so that I didn't get them in my line of fire.

Behind me the prisoners with the other three guards' guns opened fire. As the Italians dropped to the sand, more prisoners rushed forwards to grab the fallen guards' weapons. The Italians were now in terrible confusion. Some of the prisoners had dragged the drivers of the lorries out of their cabs.

As we were running towards Bessie, some Italian soldiers appeared out of their tents, guns at the ready. I let off a burst at them, hitting one in the legs, while Chalky scrambled into Bessie's co-driver's seat. He started up the Browning machine gun, maintaining constant fire, shooting a stream of bullets across the Italians' position to hold them down and keep them from returning fire.

The rest of the crew took this opportunity to climb up on to the hull, and into the turret. Once they were all inside the tank, I ran for the driver's compartment, firing as I went. George opened up with his machine gun, and he and Chalky hammered bullets into the Italians' tents and vehicles as I jumped up on to Bessie's hull and dropped down into my driver's seat.

About a hundred yards away the lorries were now full with prisoners and were being driven off.

In between machine-gun bursts we could hear shouting in Italian as an officer tried to restore some sort of order to the situation.

I pulled on my headphones and throat mike set and heard Weston order: "Right. Let's get this thing started up."

It was then I discovered that we were out of petrol.

No Way Out

"Sorry, sir," I reported. "No fuel."

Through my headphones I heard George swear. Then he said, "I'll get some. I know where they keep their fuel supply. I've had nothing better to do for days but work out the lie of this rotten camp."

"How far is it?" asked Weston.

"About a hundred yards away, over by those parked-up lorries.

If you can cover me and keep them down I should be all right."

"We'll cover you," said Weston. "Right men. Hit them with the machine guns, one gun at a time, Atkins first, then White, for five-second bursts, and keep firing alternately in that order. Fire."

Harry opened fire for his five-second burst, and then he stopped. Chalky took over, and then Harry carried on, and so on. Meanwhile we heard the metal clonk of the hatch flipping back as George clambered out. He slid down the turret and jumped down to the sand. Soon I saw him out of my hatch window, dodging and zigzagging, running for the lorries. I saw the ground behind him start to flick up as bullets thudded into it, just missing him. Then George threw himself at the lorries and rolled into cover.

"He's going to have a difficult time getting back, sir," I told Weston. "There's an open patch of ground which they've got their sights on. They nearly got him the first time. When he returns he'll be carrying two heavy cans of petrol. He'll be an easy target."

"Where's their shooting coming from?" asked Weston.

"Hard to tell, sir," I said. "We've got most of them pinned down so they can't fire directly at us, but I reckon there's someone in that tent to our left. They're right next to the fuel dump and they've got a clean line of fire to just in front of the lorries."

"Can you hit that tent, Atkins? White?" asked Weston.

"Only the top of it, sir," said Harry. "I can't hit it low, which is where their rifles will be."

"Same problem for me, sir," added Chalky. "Those armoured cars are in the way. If the Italians are lying down on the ground, they're safe."

"We have to do something, sir," I said. "George won't make it back across that open stretch."

"Maybe we could hit the tent with our main gun, sir," suggested Prof.

"Not a good idea, Read," commented Weston. "At this close range we'd likely blow up their fuel dump and Gunner

Hoskins with it. No, someone's going to have to get closer and deal with the problem."

"I'll do it, sir," I volunteered.

"I will, sir," added Harry.

"Smith volunteered first. He goes," said Weston.

"Begging your pardon, sir," put in Harry, "but Smith is our driver. If anything should go wrong, we're going to need him to get this tank back to our own lines."

"Begging your pardon, sir," I said, "but White is our co-driver. He could take Bessie back."

"Let's hope it doesn't come to that," said Weston. "Atkins, White, begin covering fire on my mark. "Ready, Smith?"

I hefted the machine gun in my hands. "Ready, sir," I said.

Chalky and Harry began firing. Quickly, I climbed up from the driver's seat and got out of the front compartment. I slid down the hull to the sand and began firing at the Italian positions. The shooting that was keeping George from getting back was coming from a tent hidden behind a couple of lorries. I ran to the lorries and dropped to the ground, then crawled under the nearest one. I kept the gun aimed at the tent at all times, just in case someone started shooting at me.

Chalky and Harry were doing a good job, with a constant stream of fire making sure the Italians' attention stayed on them. I wondered how much ammunition they had left.

I looked out from under the other side of the lorry towards the fuel dump. George was crouched down behind the drums of petrol. It wasn't exactly the safest hiding place; one bullet and he'd go up with nothing left of him but ashes. George saw me under the lorry and he gestured at the two cans of petrol he'd got hold of. I gave him a thumbs up.

George pointed at the tent where the shooting was coming from and then held up three fingers. So there were three of them in there with their guns aimed at the open area. I guessed they wouldn't shoot at George while he was in cover behind the fuel drums. They'd kill him all right, but they'd also lose all their fuel and risk blowing themselves up in the process. I was hoping that all their attention would be concentrated on the fuel dump, waiting for George to come out on his return trip.

I inched forwards on my stomach from under cover of the lorry and worked my way flat on the sand, holding the gun in front of me, towards the tent. Chalky and Harry maintained their constant firing from the tank, keeping the other Italians' attention on them. I worked my way round to just in front of the flap of the tent, trying not to make any noise. Then I got to my feet, expecting at any second a burst of gunfire.

I looked across to George's position but I couldn't see him now – he was hidden behind the fuel drums. I hoped he'd be listening and would know that when I started shooting it was the signal for him to make his move. I checked the gun one last time, and then I fired at just above ground level through the canvas of the tent. After a few seconds I took a quick look inside. They'd been caught by surprise. My burst had hit them low and all three of them were lying on the ground, groaning and clutching their legs.

Out of the corner of my eye I saw George start his run, a can of petrol hanging from each hand, and I began to cover the tents with my machine gun, moving backwards all the time, heading for the lorries. The firing from Bessie carried on, CHATTER-CHATTER-CHATTER-CHATTER-CHATTER, as Harry and Chalky fired on.

I rolled back under the lorry again and paused before sprinting back to the tank, firing all the time. George ran around to the back of Bessie, to the fuel tank.

I clambered up on to the front compartment and dropped back into my driver's seat. I was sweating like a pig. It wasn't just the heat, it was the fear.

Harry and Chalky kept up their firing for the few minutes it took for George to get the petrol into Bessie's tank, and then the sound of George's boots scraping on the hull and the clang of the hatch dropping back into place told me we were ready.

"Right, Smith!" snapped Weston. "Get us out of here."

I started Bessie up and moved her back. After we'd gone about a hundred yards, Weston ordered me to halt. He gave orders to George and Harry.

"Four medium shells into the camp," he said. "Destroy all their remaining vehicles so they can't follow us."

We heard Harry and George load their medium guns and open fire. We watched as the lorries blew up and caught fire, the fire spreading to the tents. The surviving Italian soldiers ran out from behind the burning cover, yelling and shouting, throwing caution to the winds. This was too much for them. They held their hands above their heads in surrender, afraid that we'd hit them next.

"They're surrendering, sir," I said.

"Good," said Weston. "We'll lock them up in their own compound. Then we'll take whatever fuel and ammunition we can carry. We've got a long way to go before we get home."

Under Attack

It didn't take us long to herd the few remaining Italians into their own compound and lock the gates. They'd be able to climb the wire and get out, but it would take them time. And the more time we had, the better it was for us.

We loaded some more fuel drums on to the back of Bessie's hull and replenished our stock of ammunition – both sizes of shells for the bigger guns and bullets for the machine guns – before setting off again.

It had been nearly two hours since the two Australians had staged the fight that had signalled the start of the mass escape. The lorries taking them had long gone. It was our hope that they'd been able to get back to our own lines and let our side know what had happened. As Weston said, we were a long way from home, behind enemy lines, and we could do with some help if we ran into the Axis forces on our way.

We drove in silence for a while. I took a quick look at Chalky. He still looked a bit ill. With one hand I disconnected my throat mike, and then reached out and disconnected his. Chalky looked at me, surprised, but I didn't want to make him feel worse with the other lads listening to what we had to say.

"Feeling sick?" I asked.

He nodded. "It's not the same when you kill them from a tank," he said. "You don't see them. They're just … just so far away. But when you actually see them up close, lying there, and you know that you've killed someone's husband, someone's brother, it's terrible."

"I know it's awful, but it's them or us, Chalky," I replied.

"I'll be OK," he said. "I'll just keep telling myself: they're dropping bombs on my mum, and I'll be all right. Thanks, John."

I reconnected my throat mike and gestured for Chalky to do the same.

We were all quiet in the tank after that, keeping our thoughts to ourselves and looking out for anything on the horizon. Every so often Prof would send out a radio call, hoping that he'd make contact, but with no luck. All around us the desert was empty. Empty and silent.

Bessie was a tank without markings because the Italians had never got round to painting on their colours. If anyone spotted us, she was a tank without a country.

We must have been travelling for about two hours when we heard a plane. Weston, in the open turret, took a sighting. Then he dropped down into the tank and shut the hatch.

"A Stuka," he announced over the intercom. "Full speed ahead, Smith."

We were already going as fast as we could, but I tried to get a little more out of her, knowing that we were about to be bombed by a Stuka.

The dive-bomber came low over us, checking us out. The lack of symbols obviously puzzled the pilot at first, but not for long. The Stuka turned and came back towards us, this time in a firing position.

"Gun up," ordered Weston.

George elevated the main gun as best he could, but it's almost impossible to get the right elevation for an attacking plane. The Stuka flew over us, giving us a burst with its guns as it passed over, the bullets ricocheting off our armoured hull and turret.

"Zigzag, Smith," ordered Weston.

I had been thinking of doing just that, anyway. A plane gets a line of fire to set up its bombing run. By zigzagging you can keep away from the straight bombing line, providing your tank can turn very tightly.

I began to zigzag, turning sharply to the left and then accelerating away, just as we heard the Stuka turn and come back at us from behind. I swung to the right and then to the left again. I had been lucky in the way I'd chosen. The Stuka dropped its first bomb, but it exploded away to our right and a massive shower of sand rained down on us. Too close for comfort.

We heard the drone of the Stuka's engine as it flew on. Then we saw it bank ahead of us as it turned into position for its next bombing run.

I could hear Prof urgently sending out call signs over the radio. I didn't pay much attention to what he was saying; I was concentrating on keeping Bessie moving backwards and forwards, then moving straight, before turning and zigzagging, as I tried to throw the Stuka off getting a firm sighting on us. Chalky, George and Harry opened up with their Brownings as the plane came in for its dive, doing their best to put the pilot off. The Stuka's second bomb smashed into the desert barely fifty yards away. He'd missed – but only just.

"He's getting closer," I said.

"You're doing well, Smith," said Weston over my headphones. "Keep it up."

I put Bessie through another turn … and then disaster struck! We ground to a halt!

"Smith!" yelled Weston. "What's happened?"

I revved up the engine, but Bessie wouldn't move and just sank deeper into the sand.

"I think we've hit soft sand, sir!" I yelled.

Behind us we heard the Stuka turn, flying higher now to make sure that when he came in this time he was out of range of the machine guns. Frantically, I pulled at the levers, stamped on the pedals, but to no avail. We just lurched backwards and forwards, literally stuck in a rut, while the Stuka came in for the kill on a sitting target.

Harry and George swung their guns towards the oncoming plane and hammered away, but it was useless: the Stuka had chosen its height carefully. This was like the last time, only worse. Everyone dead and all because I was a useless tank driver.

"Get us out of here, Smith!" bellowed Weston.

I started to panic as Bessie rocked uselessly on the spot … and then suddenly I knew what we had to do. It was an insane idea, but the only chance we had.

"Drop the main gun and fire into the sand, George!" I yelled.

"What?" demanded George bewildered.

"Don't argue, just do it!" I yelled.

There was a shell already in the breech. George swung the gun down as low as it would go and fired. As I felt the gun fire, I kicked Bessie into reverse and with the recoil we rocked backwards out of the sand hole. Immediately, I swung Bessie partway round and carried on reversing at speed, just as the Stuka let fly with its bomb. It landed and exploded in exactly the place where just ten seconds earlier we'd been trapped. Once again, we were covered in sand, but we had survived.

"Brilliant, John!" laughed Prof.

"Well done, Smith," complimented Weston. "But we're not out of danger yet. Here he comes again!"

The Stuka turned for its final attack. This time we also heard the sounds of more aircraft approaching, and my heart sank.

"He's called up reinforcements," came Harry's voice. "We're finished now!"

As we watched, the other planes grew larger in the sky. I could see six of them. But their wing-shapes were different. They weren't Stukas.

"They're ours!" called out Harry excitedly.

He was right. Two of the planes flew out of the formation and headed for the Stuka that was coming straight for us again. The German pilot saw them coming and turned, but not before he had released his final bomb at us. Fortunately this distraction had spoiled the bomber's aim and the bomb exploded some distance behind us.

Then the two Allied planes opened fire and we saw the Stuka take a hit. Thick black smoke poured out from its engine. It hung for a second before spinning and tumbling out of the sky, followed by an enormous explosion as it crashed into the desert a couple of miles away from us.

By now Prof was jabbering away on the radio, talking to the lead pilot of the formation. Then he relayed his conversation to Weston, and we all heard it.

"We're back behind our own lines, sir!" he said excitedly. "The Germans and Italians have been pushed back from Alamein! We're winning!"

We all burst into cheering. We'd done it! "Chaps," said Weston's cheerful voice in my headphones, "it looks like we're home!"

Home

As we neared our own front line we passed burnt-out German and Italian tanks and the ruins of Axis machine-gun posts. Barbed wire and debris were strewn around all over the place. The Axis positions had been hammered and overrun. Behind us, the Germans and Italians were now in retreat.

Weston stood up in the open hatch, a makeshift Union flag we'd found tied to the radio aerial, flying alongside him.

We passed a few divisions of our own troops moving forward, foot soldiers backed up by tanks and armoured cars. Then more soldiers and more tanks and more armoured cars. The Eighth Army was on the move, advancing just as Monty had promised.

"Maybe we ought to turn round and go the same way as everyone else, sir?" suggested George.

"We will soon enough," grinned Weston. "Once we've reported back to our unit and let them know we're safe and ready to resume action."

"Resume action, sir?" grinned Harry. "I didn't realize we'd stopped."

We were all laughing at Harry's joke, when an open car came heading straight towards us, flashing its headlights at us to stop. I eased on the brake and brought Bessie to a halt. The car pulled up right in front of us, and a major climbed out from the back and stood staring at Bessie.

"What is this tank doing out of uniform?" he demanded.

We all tried not to laugh out loud. Weston was the only one who kept a straight face.

"It's a rather long story, sir," he said.

He was just starting to tell the major about our adventures, when another car appeared, a cloud of sand and dust trailing behind it. Immediately the major sprang to attention and saluted, as did Weston. The second car pulled up and down from it stepped Monty himself.

"At ease!" ordered Monty crisply.

All around us, everyone had stopped. All vehicles, all foot soldiers, everything. Everyone was watching Monty as he surveyed Bessie. Weston dropped down from the hatch on to the sand and saluted.

"Lieutenant Weston and Tank Crew 247 reporting for duty, sir!"

"Good," said Monty.

Monty studied Bessie for a moment, noticing the painted-out insignia and the marks of damage. Then he came round to the driver's hatch and looked at me.

I saluted as best I could from my position, and I thought I saw a twinkle in his eye.

"Driver Smith," said Monty, "we meet again. I see you are in possession of an unusual tank. Stolen?"

"No, sir," I replied. "It's ours. We recaptured it from the Italians and brought it back. We thought it might come in handy!"

Behind Monty's back, the major looked like he was about to turn purple in the face with anger. Monty gave a little smile.

"Quite right," he said. "From now on we're going to need all the tanks we can get! We're going on to victory!"

With that, he turned to the major and said: "I want every one of these men in this tank recommended for military honours. These are the kind of men I want in my army. Give me men like these and we'll win this war. Heroes, every one. Make a note of their names."

The major swallowed, astonished at this sudden turn of events. Then he saluted.

"Yes, sir," he said.

"Good," said Monty crisply. "Carry on."

Monty strode back to his car, got in and drove off.

The major stood looking at us for a few seconds, still unable to come to terms with what he had just seen and heard, and then he turned to his adjutant and ordered: "You heard the C-in-C, Brownlow. Get their names. They're heroes."

And when they heard those words, all the men standing around, whether on foot, or in jeeps or in tanks, began to cheer and came over to shake our hands. Crew 247 had come home.

EL ALAMEIN AND AFTER

John Smith's story was set during the period of the Battle of El Alamein. In fact, this was a series of battles which lasted from July 1942 until early November 1942. After a number of fierce attacks and counter-attacks by both sides around the area of El Alamein, the Allies finally broke out in November 1942, forcing the Axis forces to retreat.

During November and December 1942 the Eighth Army advanced from El Alamein to El Agheila, pushing the Axis forces back. This was the first occasion in the desert war when the Germans had been in retreat for such a length of time. The retreat by the Axis forces went on right through the winter and into the spring of 1943.

The Allied advance continued up to May 1943, with the German forces fighting all the way in their forced retreat across North Africa. Towards the end of this campaign the Eighth Army was joined by American and French forces of United States II Corps following a sea landing. Finally, the end of all Axis resistance in North Africa came on 12 May. The war in the North African desert was over.

THE SIGNIFICANCE OF EL ALAMEIN

Up until the victory at El Alamein, the Allies had been losing the Second World War. The victory at El Alamein had a threefold effect:

• It showed that the might of the German army could be defeated, and in this way raised morale throughout the rest of the Allied forces.

• It secured the Suez Canal for the Allies as a vital supply line.

• It led directly to the successful Italian campaign, with Montgomery's forces and the American forces under General Mark Clark moving on from North Africa to conquer Italy, forcing the Italians to surrender.

BEHIND ENEMY LINES

THE FALL OF BURMA

Burma was part of Britain's huge colonial territory in south-east Asia. Because the British Military Command didn't believe that the Japanese would seriously consider invading Burma, only a small force was allocated to defend the territory, which consisted of a few small British units and the locally recruited 1st Burma Division. Both were poorly equipped and inadequately trained.

In December 1941 Burma and Malaysia were invaded by the Japanese. They intended to cut the supply links between the British and their Chinese allies, as well as securing a stronghold in south-east Asia from which they could dominate the Pacific. The success of these two initial attacks led the Japanese to increase their invasion army. By mid-March 1942 the British in Burma were in full retreat. Along with the fleeing British forces were thousands of refugees, British colonials being driven out of the country. This long retreat through Burma back to India was one of the major Allied disasters of the Asian front during the Second World War. By the end of May 1942 Burma was entirely in Japanese hands and the British had experienced a defeat which had cost over 13,500 lives and left Japan in firm control of British colonial territory in south-east Asia.

Even with the Americans now fighting in the Pacific war, the Allied Military Commanders believed that Burma was lost and that the Japanese were almost invincible in the Asian jungles. One man had a different view. Orde Wingate had successfully used guerrilla warfare tactics in North Africa in the early days of the war. He now proposed setting up LRP (Long Range Penetration) Groups to go into Burma behind enemy lines. These forces would sabotage railway lines, bridges, etc, and cause major disruption to the Japanese. The way would then be prepared for an Allied invasion to be launched and Burma to be recaptured. Many Military High Commanders believed this proposal was doomed to failure. However, with the support of Prime Minister Winston Churchill, and the commander-in-chief in India and Asia, Sir Archibald Wavell, Wingate put together his LRP Groups, and in early 1943 he and 3,000 men (known as "the Chindits") slipped into Burma against the 80,000 strong, and so far invincible, Japanese army.

COMMANDO SUPPLIES AND RATIONS

At the start of the Chindit operation, each man of the 77th Indian Infantry Brigade carried a pack with enough rations for five days, consisting of twelve biscuits, some nuts, raisins and dates, two ounces of cheese, tea, sugar and milk. Each man was also allowed one blanket.

Instead of carrying tents, the Chindits built their own shelters on site from branches, grass and large leaves.

Each brigade had mules equipped with specially made solid leather panniers, measuring 1 metre by 30 cm by 30 cm. These mules carried the vital signalling equipment. It took four mules to carry one set of wireless equipment, as follows:

Mule no. 1: a radio set on one side, balanced with a spare set in the pannier on the other side
Mule no. 2: the battery-charging unit, balanced with two petrol cans in the pannier on the other side (when

a two gallon tank was empty it was filled with water to balance the load)

Mule no. 3: 48 amp hour battery on each side

Mule no. 4: pannier on each side for other communications equipment (e.g. electrician's kit, oil for the charging unit, water and acid for the batteries, earphones, keys for sending, aerial, rope and spare copper wire, message pads, operating light for night work, groundsheet)

Caught!

Night-time in the jungle. I lay hidden in the long grass. About fifty yards in front of me was a river, crossed by a rickety wooden bridge. A vital link in the Japanese supply line. My task was simple – to blow it up. Me, Lieutenant John Smith of 142 Commando. I was on my own, since a large force would be spotted more easily than just one man. In the bag slung around my neck was my equipment: timer pencils, wire and plastic explosives, all wrapped in waterproof oilskin. I was light on weapons, just a Colt automatic pistol and my fighting knife.

Ahead of me trees, bushes and long rushes lined the river. Then there was a mudbank, and then the river itself.

I decided to approach the bridge using the river: the current would take me downriver until I was near enough to the wooden supports that held up the middle of the bridge.

I edged forward, keeping flat, using my elbows and knees to move along in a crawl, which gave me a slight snake-like zigzag movement through the grass.

There were guards patrolling the bridge, the moonlight glinting on the barrels of their rifles. Ten yards to go before I made it to the cover of the trees. Eight yards. Five. Four.

Just past these trees and then down into the river. I moved forward, crouching low. Suddenly I glimpsed a movement just behind me out of the corner of my eye. Before I could turn and defend myself a boot behind my knee knocked my legs from under me. The next second I was sprawled face down on the ground, one arm pulled savagely and painfully up between my shoulder blades, the sharp blade of a knife pressed against my throat. A harsh voice rattled out in Japanese, "Sayonara!" Then the voice changed to a soft Scottish burr and added: "That's Japanese for goodbye. You're dead, mate."

Sergeant Ross stood up and let me clamber to my feet. He put his knife away and shook his head sorrowfully as he looked at me.

"Lieutenant Smith, ye may be a very whizz at blowing up things, but ye still have a lot to learn about the jungle."

As I walked back to my tent after that first training session with my two pals, Cookie Watson and Billy McDermott, I could still feel the sense of humiliation and anger at myself for having been caught so easily. Me, a trained commando. Billy saw the expression on my face and grinned.

"Don't be so hard on yourself, John," he said. "It was your first day of jungle training."

"It was your first day as well, but you didn't get caught like I did," I pointed out.

"That's because I come from a background where you start creeping through forests while you're still wearing nappies." Billy smiled.

Billy was from Kenya and had spent much of his youth hunting with his father out in the African bush. As a result, Billy could sit for hours in a jungle, barely moving, waiting for his prey to come along. He was small and wiry, his skin browned and leathery from his years spent outside in the sun. His hair was black and thick, and with his sharp pointed features he looked a bit like a jungle animal himself.

Cookie Watson, on the other hand, was tall and blond, with a snub nose, freckles and a perpetual cheery grin.

"So what if we can creep through forests better than you," added Cookie Watson. "You're the best at blowing things up."

"It's important to me because I'm the lieutenant of this unit," I retorted. "I'm supposed to be in charge."

"So what?" shrugged Cookie. "Brigadier Wingate's in charge of the whole shooting match, but I bet he can't blow up a bridge as well as you can, or cook a hedgehog in mud as well as I can."

Cookie had got his name because of his amazing ability to make a meal out of anything. Hedgehog. Lizard. Even maggots. Cookie could survive on almost anything. He said the aborigines had taught him how. Cookie was from Australia. Like many others from the British Empire countries, Australia, New Zealand, South Africa, Canada and Rhodesia, he and Billy had returned to Britain at the start of the war to join up.

All three of us were the same age, nineteen years old, and had been together in the commandos for the last six months. We'd trained in Scotland together and we trusted each other with our lives, a special bond that comes when you work so closely together and depend on each other for your very survival.

Reluctantly I accepted what Cookie said: just because you were in charge it didn't mean you had to be the best at absolutely everything.

"Remember," Billy pointed out, "me and Cookie both come from tropical climes, but this is the first time you've been in the jungle.

There was some truth in what Billy said. Most of the training missions I'd been on had involved sea-landings or had been carried out not far from the coast. This one was different. And we were also up against the Japanese.

"The way I see it," said Cookie, "the real problem with this operation is we're going to be depending on so many other blokes who aren't us. You know, who aren't trained commandos. Most of them aren't even volunteers, they've been conscripted into the army and have no choice in the matter."

"Not all of them," I said. "Anyway, the Gurkhas and the Burmese are all volunteers."

"Yeah, but they're not trained like we are," continued Cookie.

"They don't need to be," put in Billy. "Burma is their country. They know it already, they don't need to be trained how to survive in the jungle."

"I do," I said ruefully, still smarting over the way I'd let myself be caught by Sergeant Ross.

Cookie grinned. "Don't worry, John," he said. "Me and Billy will be with you. You just take care of blowing things up."

As I slipped into my sleeping bag that night I checked my watch. Four hours to grab some sleep, and then up at dawn for more training. As I drifted off to sleep, I could still feel the blade of Sergeant Ross's knife at my throat.

For the next few weeks we trained in jungle techniques at the Bush Warfare School in the Indian jungle. Along with learning how to live off the jungle for food, shelter and fresh water, we continued to practise the skills we specialized in. In my case this was demolition. Blowing up bridges, buildings and trains using the minimum amount of explosive to achieve the maximum effect. Anyone can blow something up using tons of explosives, but often they also destroy everything and everyone else in the area. If you're blowing up a bridge you have to know the bridge to be able to identify where the key supports are.

Everybody attached to our unit – the 77th Indian Infantry Brigade – was keen to knuckle down and learn, except Private Peter Parker. Private Parker was a conscript, and a moaner. He mumbled constantly in low tones to himself about how unfair this war was to him. Private Parker didn't want to be here in India, didn't want to be in the army. He wanted to be back home in Liverpool, painting roads and park fences and working for the City Council. He wasn't happy out here. The reason I knew all about Private Parker's feelings was because he was attached to my small unit.

The 77th Indian Infantry Brigade, also known as the Chindits, was made up of a regiment of British soldiers, the 13th Kings Liverpool Regiment; divisions of Gurkhas from the 3/2nd Gurkha Rifles; Burmese and border Indian tribesmen from the Karen, Kachin and Chin tribes, who made up the 2nd Burma Rifles; a section of mule handlers; and those of us from 142 Commando Company. In addition there were about a dozen pilots from the RAF who would be flying supplies in to us once we were behind enemy lines.

The brigade was split into seven columns, with soldiers from all the different regiments mixed up in each column. Within each column there were smaller units. Mine was made up of Cookie, Billy, two Burmese soldiers, Maung and Kyan, Private Parker and myself. Ba Maung and Tig Kyan were both quiet men, fiercely keen to get back into Burma and rid their homeland of the Japanese. Especially Ba Maung, whose whole family had been killed by the Japanese when Burma was invaded. All Private Parker wanted to do was go home.

After six weeks of solid training there was a new feeling of purpose at the training school. All of us, with the exception of Private Parker and a few of his like-minded cronies, were fit, confident and straining at the leash to go into action. We didn't have to wait long. Late one afternoon towards the end of January, our whole brigade, all 3,000 men, were called to assemble in the grounds of the Warfare School for a briefing.

Most of us sat cross-legged on the ground; others found seats or positions on the low branches of trees. It was as if we were an audience preparing to watch an open-air show out here in a clearing in the jungle. The star of this particular show tonight strode into the clearing now, a bearded man, short and wiry. Brigadier Orde Wingate.

Wingate had a presence about him, there was no denying that. Everyone who ever came into contact with Wingate remarked on it. The word was most of the top brass, except for Wavell and Mountbatten, disliked Wingate. For one thing he didn't dress up in smart, newly ironed uniforms and parade around. Apparently one senior officer had been heard to remark that Wingate looked like he put his clothes on with a shovel. Nor was Wingate seen in smart officer circles. Wingate was a man dedicated to soldiering, to fighting and winning battles.

With a map hung from a frame erected between some trees, Orde Wingate turned to face us.

"Well, men," he said. "I'm glad you're all fit and well and have had a good rest at this holiday camp."

There was the usual laughter and groans that Wingate expected at this remark.

"I'm pleased to tell you that, after all the waiting we've

endured, we're finally about to go into action. Behind enemy lines."

He produced a stick and banged one of the maps fixed to the trees.

"Burma!" he announced. "Full of Japanese soldiers at the moment: 80,000 of them. We think we know where the big sections of them are, but it's difficult to tell with certainty from our reconnaissance because of the thick jungle. We're going to cross into Burma in columns, each column with a different objective. Our supplies will be carried either by mules, or by ourselves. Contact between each group will be by wireless. We'll also use wireless to arrange for the RAF to drop supplies as needed, but you'd better make very sure of your position. We don't want the supplies being dropped into enemy hands.

"This operation has three main aims. One, to cut the main railway line between Mandalay and Myitkyina and put a halt to Japanese supplies getting easily to their troops. Two, to harass the Japanese at every opportunity, particularly in the Shwebo area. Three, to cross the Irrawaddy, travel south and cut the railway line between Mandalay and Lashio."

Wingate paced around, looking at us, and it was as if his intense eyes pierced every man there.

"This isn't going to be a picnic. We hope we can get you all safely into Burma. IV Corps have done their best to secure a safe front on this side of the Chindwin River, although there are no guarantees that the Japanese won't be hiding in the jungle waiting for us when we land on the other side. I have to tell you, however, that there are no plans for getting us back safely. Once we have achieved our objectives it'll be up to every man to make his own way back to base here in India, or up towards the Chinese border. The Japanese will be hunting for us with everything they've got. But we can defeat them. And we can get away. Because we are the 77th Indian Infantry Brigade, the best damned force in the whole British army!"

At this there rose a great roar of approval from the crowd, 3,000 men waving their arms and cheering.

"We must all be as mad as he is!" grinned Cookie.

"Of course we are," I said. "Otherwise we wouldn't have volunteered to be here!"

A week later, after a march of 130 miles, we were at Imphal in Assam, within thirty miles of the Burmese border. We had covered the distance in a series of night-time marches to avoid being spotted by Japanese reconnaissance planes. Once we got to Imphal the brigade separated into its seven columns. Wingate had planned a many-pronged attack, with each column heading into Burma from a different direction, some coming in from the north, some at different points from the west. The one thing every column had to do was to cross the Chindwin River, the wide river which marked the boundary between India and Japanese-held Burma.

Our column headed due east into the jungle that bordered the Chindwin for a depth of many miles on the Indian side.

We spent the next two days travelling under dense cover. It was a tall order, trying to move 400 men, mules and equipment through territory like this without being observed by possible Japanese spies in the area. All the time I had Private Parker just a few paces behind me, muttering under his breath and wishing he wasn't here. Billy suggested I transfer Parker to another unit and let them suffer his complaining, but I felt it would show failure on my part, admitting that I couldn't control the men under my command. At one point Cookie threatened to throw Parker in a swamp unless he shut up with his whining, so from then Parker kept quiet and just kept a sour look on his face.

We came out of the jungle at the narrow point where there was a bend in the river. It was about 400 yards to the opposite bank. From our position we could see about three miles in either direction, upriver and downriver. That meant that if the enemy were hidden somewhere in the thick jungle on the opposite bank, watching for us, they'd be able to see us cross. Once we were in the middle of the river in our small, unstable rubber boats, we'd be sitting targets. There was also the problem of climbing up the steep bank on the other side of the river.

"Ready, Lieutenant?" asked our company commander, Major Rawns beside me.

"I was just wondering about the bank opposite, sir," I commented. "It looks pretty difficult."

"Let's worry about that once we get over the river," said Rawns. "Send the men over."

I went over in the first boat with Cookie, Tig Kyan, Private Parker, and coils of rope and equipment. We had a rope tied to the boat so that it could be hauled back and used again.

Once we were away from the bank we had to paddle tremendously hard because there was a strong undercurrent beneath the surface of the river that dragged our tiny boat downstream. We were so busy fighting the strong current that we almost forgot about the Japanese guns that might have been trained on us from the other bank. Almost, but not completely.

Finally we made it across. Cookie leapt out and held the boat steady while Parker, Tig Kyan and I unloaded it. Then we fixed a length of rope to the other end of the boat and hooked it round the branch of a tree. This was the first stage in constructing a ferry. That done, we signalled to the men on the far bank, and they began to haul the boat back using their rope. The three other rubber boats were making the crossing, the men in them paddling at speed, confident that there were no Japanese lurking in the bushes. Soon we had a makeshift ferry operating using all four small rubber boats to bring a squad of sappers and their supplies across.

Now the work began in earnest. Getting a small group of men over by this ferry system was one thing, getting the rest of the men, the mules, and the heavy equipment was quite another. For that we had to bring thick cable ropes across. Meanwhile, the sappers were hard at work on both sides of the river, making rafts from any timber available.

Finally, the strong power lines were stretched as taut as they could be across the river, the rafts were ready, and the mass crossing began. Throughout the rest of the afternoon the rubber boats went backwards and forwards, as did the rafts, using the power lines as pulleys. Most of the mules swam across the river. Those mules that were reluctant to swim over were tied to the rafts and towed along behind them as they crossed.

While all this was going on, Tig Kyan and I were reconnoitring the steep and muddy riverbank, looking for the best route. At last we found it: a small stream running off the Chindwin. The rivulet turned dry after a few yards and became a gulley, sloping gradually upwards.

"Here," announced Tig confidently, pointing upwards into the dense jungle beyond.

I hurried back and reported to Major Rawns, and our column set off along this gulley in single file, every sense alert. From this moment we were in Japanese-held territory, behind enemy lines.

Jungle Massacre

At first light next morning our wireless operator made contact with Wingate's column, the brigade's mobile HQ. We learnt that four of the other columns had made it safely across the river and, like us, were heading behind enemy lines. Two of the columns, however, hadn't been so lucky. The column entering Burma from the north had been a sitting target for the Japanese as they'd tried to cross the river. Casualties had been catastrophic. About half the column had died there in the river, while those on the far bank could only watch helplessly and fire at the enemy hidden in the jungle, doing their best to try and avoid hitting their own men.

Another column, the one that had crossed the Chindwin about ten miles further north from us, had been ambushed by Japanese troops within five miles of getting into Burma. Fifteen men were dead and the rest had been broken up into smaller units. Most of them were now retreating, heading back towards the Chindwin with the Japanese in close pursuit, though there were reports that some of them had decided to press on into Burma, hoping to join up with one of the other columns and carry on with the mission.

"Poor blokes," commented Billy glumly when we heard this news.

"It's not all bad, though, is it?" put in Parker. "I mean, for us it's a good thing. After all, while the Japs are chasing them they're not chasing us."

A hard look from me shut him up.

We broke up our camp so that we wouldn't leave any traces of our presence, and then we set off into the depths of the jungle.

Sunlight filtered down through the broad leaves of the huge teak trees as we marched. A light mist rose from the soft marshy ground. It could have been a peaceful scene, except for our fully armed column working their way along the jungle floor, and the thought that somewhere in the jungle there were Japanese troops.

As we marched, the damp heat of the jungle clung to us, mixing with the sweat from our bodies. Our clothes stuck to us. And all the time the flies and mosquitoes buzzed, crawling over our skin and biting. I did my best to swat them away, but after a while I realized there were just too many of them and let them get on with it.

It had been hot and humid in the Indian jungle. Here, in Burma, it was even worse. Without our acclimatization time in India, this jungle would have killed us with heatstroke.

Keeping constantly on the alert, we marched through this

terrain at quite a fast pace. Now and then our column halted when the soldier on point thought he heard a noise ahead, or there was a flurry of activity in the depths of the jungle to the side of us, but these were either jungle birds or animals. Our progress seemed almost too good to be true. It was. We hit our first major obstacle after we'd been marching for three hours: a swamp of black mud that stretched out in front of us, and seemed to go on for miles both to our left and to our right.

Taking the initiative, Johnson, one of the sappers, edged carefully forward towards the swamp, making sure he trod where the rushes grew and the ground should have been fairly firm, but he only managed three paces before he began to sink into the oozing black slime. Immediately the soldier behind him, Attridge, grabbed hold of the sapper to pull him out. It wasn't enough, Johnson was sinking further in the mud. Other soldiers grabbed hold of Attridge and a human chain was formed that hauled both men backwards slowly but surely. At last Johnson was pulled clear on to firm ground.

His clothes were black with mud right up to his armpits.

"Thanks, mate," he muttered hoarsely to Attridge. "I wouldn't have fancied ending my days in that lot."

As the relieved Johnson changed into dry clothes and recovered from his terrifying ordeal, Major Rawns assessed the situation.

"Right," he announced. "Two patrols. One to the east, one to the west. We've got to find a way round this swamp. Smith, take your unit to the east. Anderson, yours to the west."

Steve Anderson and I nodded. He set off one way with his unit, and I led Cookie, Billy, Ba Maung, Tig Kyan and Parker off in the opposite direction. We followed the edge of the swamp for about an hour. All the time we had to watch where we put our feet in case the swamp had penetrated the ground beneath us. After five miles it became obvious that there was no way round the swamp in our direction. At least, from our observations, not within the next mile or so, or possibly more.

We returned to the column and made our report. Anderson and his west patrol joined us about an hour later with the same bad news. There was no way round. We either had to go back and strike another route, or cross the swamp. We had already lost valuable time looking for another route.

"How far do you think it is across this swamp, Captain Hayes?" asked the major.

Captain Hayes looked thoughtfully across at the jungle.

"Difficult to say, Major," he said. "A hundred yards across this first bit to those trees, at least. But who's to say what's beyond that?"

"Only one way to find out," said the major. "One thing's

for sure, we're not going back." He turned to the rest of the column and called out: "Right, men. We're going to make a causeway. Start cutting down some of the thinner trees!"

So we set to work, cutting down some of the thinnest but tall trees, and then cut them into lengths. We spread these out on the surface of the swamp, criss-crossing them and filling in the holes between them with brushwood, rushes and small branches. Yard by yard we pushed out from solid ground, adding piece by piece of jungle timber and greenery to our causeway. It took us about two hours of back-breaking and wet and muddy work, but by the end of it we had a road of sorts across the black mud. It took us another two hours to cross it, one soldier at a time so that the causeway wouldn't sink into the mud under too much weight. I was the third man to cross over it, and at every step the rough timber construction moved, sinking into and sliding over the mud, and every second I thought it would give way. The mules were reluctant to cross it – they hated the feel of the ground beneath their hooves slipping and sliding unsteadily, but with some strong pulling and tough persuasion the mule-handlers got them across.

The heavier equipment was spread out into the four rubber boats, and then each of these was hauled across the surface of the swamp by a soldier moving as fast as he could across the makeshift causeway in order to keep the boat moving, slurping and slipping on the mud surface.

At last, with everyone over, we set off through teak jungle once more. We had barely travelled half a mile when we hit swamp again. As before, there was no way round. Once again we set to work, chopping trees and gathering brushwood to make a jungle causeway. Over the next four miles we did this six times. By the time darkness descended and we got ready to make camp for the night, we were bone-weary and covered in mud. The only lucky thing, to our thinking, was that no self-respecting Japanese would want to come into this swamp-ridden part of the jungle.

Dawn the next day found our column already on the move. Each unit took turns on point. It was late morning when my unit moved to the front of the column. We edged forward cautiously through the jungle. Tig Kyan and I were at the front, Billy and Parker a few yards behind, and Cookie and Ba Maung brought up the rear. Cookie, Billy and I were all armed with tommy guns, the Thomson sub-machine gun, which had become standard issue for commandos. Parker, Ba Maung and Tig Kyan all carried Lee Enfield rifles. I strained my ears, listening for sounds ahead which might give us warning of a Japanese patrol, but the thickness of the jungle made it difficult to pick anything out. We'd travelled about two miles this way, moving slowly, guns cocked, all senses alert, when we heard a loud noise dead ahead. It sounded like someone howling in agony, and it was so painful to listen to it made the hair on the back of my neck stand up.

Aware that we might be walking into a trap, I gestured for Billy and me to go first and the others to keep at a safe distance behind us, but keep us in sight.

Billy and I crept through dense trees and bushes until we saw a little ahead of us what looked like a clearing. The howling was becoming louder, more intense. After a few more paces we made the clearing, but hid behind the cover of the trees, our tommy guns ready to fire at the first sign of trouble. What we actually saw in the clearing filled me with a cold anger. A Burmese woman was kneeling, sobbing over the bodies of two children.

Behind her, the bamboo huts of the homestead had been torn down and destroyed. Scattered around in the clearing were three other bodies. And, tied to four stakes in the clearing, were the bodies of four British soldiers.

The woman looked up and screamed as Billy and I stepped out of the trees. Then Tig Kyan appeared from the jungle and spoke in Burmese, which calmed the woman down. Cookie, Ba Maung and Parker had come out into the clearing, and stood horrified at the sight which met their eyes. While Tig Kyan talked to the woman, doing his best to calm her down and find out her story, I turned to Parker and Ba Maung.

"Report back to Major Rawns and the rest of the column," I said. "Tell them what's happened here and warn them that Japanese soldiers may still be patrolling in the area."

Parker turned and hurried off into the jungle, the look on his face showing he was relieved to be leaving this scene. Ba Maung followed, the fire in his eyes showing his anger and hatred at what the Japanese had done here.

Cookie, Billy and I surveyed the ruined homestead. Two Burmese men, a woman and the two children were dead, as well as the four British soldiers.

It was pretty obvious to me that the soldiers were from the column that had been ambushed ten miles north of us. They'd been trying to find our column to join us and had come across this place. The village people had given them shelter, only for the Japanese to track them down.

"But why kill the local people?" asked Cookie, bewildered. "And why leave just her alive?"

We got the answer from Tig Kyan after he'd finished talking to the distraught woman.

"The woman's name is An Po," Tig Kyan told us. "What happened here is a message to all other Burmese. The Japanese left her alive so that she could tell others what will happen to them if they help the British soldiers."

Noises now came from the jungle behind us, and we turned, guns at the ready in case it was the Japanese coming back, but it was simply the rest of our column reaching the clearing. The looks on their faces as they surveyed the scene showed the same revulsion that we felt.

I told Major Rawns what had happened here, and indicated An Po, who was once again kneeling over the bodies of her dead children.

"The only survivor, sir," I explained.

Rawns's face darkened with anger. He then composed himself and gave his orders.

"Deal with the bodies," he said. "Decent burial for our men. Find out from your Burmese what the proper rites are for their people, and follow them accordingly. These people died for us, it's the least they deserve."

"What about the woman, sir?" I asked.

"We'll take her with us until we come to a safe village and we'll leave her there," said Rawns. Turning to Captain Hayes, he added, "Captain, pass the following order along the lines. Whatever happens, in future our men are not to use local people to seek shelter. I won't give the Japanese the excuse to commit this kind of atrocity again."

"Yes, sir," said the captain.

"We'll camp here tonight," added Rawns. "Send some of the men to check out the area for a good drop site. Then wireless Base and tell them we'll take a supply drop at first light tomorrow morning. We'll give them the co-ordinates later after we've chosen the site."

"Very good, sir," said Hayes.

Ba Maung told us that the people had been Buddhists, so he and the other Burmese in our column held a brief but proper Buddhist funeral for their dead. We buried the bodies of the four British soldiers.

After the ceremonies I took Parker and Tig Kyan to check for a good drop site.

Others set to work to make our camp, hacking and cutting at brushwood and trees. As always, camp was made off the beaten track, the unit splitting up and building temporary shelters in the jungle itself from the surrounding trees and creepers. These shelters were usually situated about

500 yards into the jungle off the track, far enough away not to be spotted by any passing patrols, but near enough to get into action fast.

Meanwhile the radio operator sent a message to Wingate's Mobile Base over the wireless, giving a list of supplies needed.

This business of supplies being dropped to us by air was the main tactic behind Wingate's Long Range Penetration plan. Wingate's strategy was for us to travel as light as possible, carrying with us just enough food and ammunition for four or five days. Then every few days we'd radio our position and the RAF would drop us fresh supplies. Accuracy on these supply drops was all-important. If our supplies fell into Japanese hands, it could tell them many things about us: how big our strength was, our approximate position and what sort of weapons we were carrying. Losing our supply drop would also mean that we would be stranded in a hostile jungle, surrounded by the enemy, without food and ammunition. That was not a situation any of us wanted to be in.

At first light the next morning, exactly as ordered, two RAF planes came over and the parachutes with the crates beneath them floated down from the sky. We watched them from our guard positions around the drop site, which was a clearing of about 500 yards wide of firm soil, chosen so that the supplies didn't sink into muddy ground. We were positioned around the perimeter of the drop site, guns pointing into the jungle, ready to protect our supplies should the Japanese launch an attack.

While the supplies were being unpacked and loaded on to the mules, Major Rawns called me into the clearing. He was studying a map of the area, with sections marked according to information gathered from Burmese tribesmen and those who'd fled the country at the time of the Japanese invasion.

"Right, Lieutenant," said Rawns. "This is where you and your boys come into their own." He tapped a line marked on the map.

"This is our first objective, the railway line that connects Mandalay and Myitkyina." He tapped another point, about fifteen miles north-west of the railway line. "We are here. According to this map the terrain shouldn't be too difficult. We should be able to reach it by late afternoon. We'll make camp, and then tonight you'll take a small unit and blow the line up. And, after what happened here, let's do something spectacular. Show the Japs we mean business. What do you think you can do?"

I studied the map, checking the route of the railway line. It was all on flat ground, which made it difficult. The best way to take out a railway line with any long-term effect is to take out the area around it, either a bridge that supports it, or a tunnel that goes over it. There seemed to be neither on this particular stretch, just a railway line cut through the jungle. However, I had one idea.

"I'd like to talk to the woman survivor, sir," I said. "If we can find out the troop movements along the railway line, we might be able to do some major damage involving more than just the railway line."

"Find out and report back to me," said Rawns.

I saluted and hurried over to where Ba Maung was sitting with An Po, talking to her. She still seemed to be in a state of shock, but Ba Maung had calmed her down by taking turns with Tig Kyan to keep watch over her during the night, such was her fear that the Japanese might return.

"Ba Maung," I said. "We're going to blow the railway line."

"Kill Japanese?" he asked.

"That depends on what she can tell us," I said. "Ask her if she knows about the railway line. How often do trains pass along it? Once a day? Every two days? How big are the trains? Do they carry soldiers?"

Ba Maung saw what I was getting at and began to question An Po. When she realized that I intended to blow the railway line up, and possibly a trainload of Japanese soldiers with it, she was only too keen to co-operate.

Ba Maung discovered that a train came along the line every three days with supplies for the troops to the north.

Usually there was one carriage filled with soldiers to guard the supplies, as well as other soldiers stationed at intervals along the length of the train. The next supply train was due to pass along the line tomorrow morning.

I passed this information back to Major Rawns, and filled him in on my proposal: not only to destroy the railway line but also to ambush the train.

"Pay them back for what they did here to the villagers and our men," mused Rawns. "Very well, Lieutenant. But you'd better make damned sure you stop that train."

Ambush

We made good time through the jungle and by four o'clock that afternoon, according to the map, we were two miles west of the railway line.

Taking my bag of tricks with me, including my detonators, explosives and wire, I set off towards the line, accompanied by Captain Haynes and 200 armed soldiers. I took Cookie and Billy as my back-up demolition unit, and three other commandos, Reg Johnson, Dinny Wetherall and Peter Simpson. Like me, Peter was a specialist in demolition.

My plan was to set two explosions a mile apart, wrecking the line. Peter would set one charge while Dinny and Reg gave him cover. I'd set my charges while Cookie and Billy kept a watchful eye for me. Tig Kyan and six other Burmese were near by in case we ran into locals and needed a translator. The 200 soldiers would stay fifty yards further back in the jungle, ready for action if needed.

As we crept towards the railway line I kept remembering Sergeant Ross's knife at my throat, and wondered if I'd meet the same fate here. We crawled the last hundred yards on our hands and knees, making as little sound as possible. We were in luck: the Japanese obviously didn't think this piece of line was vulnerable to attack.

The stretch of track I had chosen was straight for about two miles. This meant that Peter and I could keep in sight and warn each other about any snags. The track also had a downhill gradient. I wanted this for two reasons. Firstly, guards were generally always more alert when a train was going uphill, where an attack was more likely. Secondly, when the train came off the rails I wanted it to be going at speed so that the damage would be severe. I indicated to Peter where I wanted him to lay his charges and watched him set off with Reg and Dinny.

Billy and Cookie positioned themselves in the jungle on either side of the railway line, tommy guns at the ready, watching out for any approaching enemy. Then I set to work.

I packed the explosives beneath both rails. While I was doing this, Tig Kyan came and scraped a shallow channel from the rails into the jungle. I unreeled the two lengths of detonator wire into this channel. Tig Kyan covered the wire and brushed the earth with some leaves so that it appeared untouched. I plugged the ends of the wires into the explosives and made sure they were hidden from view by taping them under the rails.

Back in the jungle I rigged up the detonator. It was quite simple: just the bare ends of two wires which, when touched together, completed an electrical circuit, triggering the explosions.

I looked along the line towards Peter. He raised his arm to let me know he had finished setting his charges. We were ready.

Soon it was pitch dark, so we settled down to wait till morning, and the arrival of the train.

When the sun came up at half past six we were all up and ready. I crouched beside my detonators. The 200 soldiers were in the jungle either side of the track between me and Peter.

The minutes passed. Seven a.m. Then eight.

The time stretched into hours. Nine o'clock came and went. Then ten. Then eleven. I began to wonder whether An Po had been right about the train. Out here in the jungle, where time meant so very little, one day was much like another and it would be easy to get confused about timings. Maybe the train had passed here the previous morning and wouldn't be passing again for another two days. Maybe the Japanese had decided not to send the train at all. All these thoughts rushed through my mind as I waited there.

Noon arrived. The hot midday sun beat down on the railway tracks, making them shimmer in the heat haze. It was sweltering. Sweat trickled down our faces and bodies and soaked our clothes.

Still there was no sign of the train.

One o'clock.

Two o'clock. No train.

Then, just as my watch was showing three o'clock, we heard the rails vibrating. A train was approaching. The news passed quickly along the two hidden lines of soldiers and immediately every man prepared for action.

The train was travelling at about thirty miles an hour. I could hear the engine hissing and steaming as it drew nearer and I could smell the smoke from its funnel. I wanted to take a look at it but dared not move in case I was spotted. I remained crouching on the edge of the jungle, hidden in the long grass. The train came nearer and nearer. As I'd hoped, it began to pick up speed as it reached the downhill section. I could see the flatbed trucks with guns mounted on them and their crews standing beside them. Then came the supply wagons, followed by a carriage filled with armed Japanese soldiers and another supply wagon. All the time I was counting the seconds, working out the position of the engine. As another flatbed truck with heavy guns mounted on it passed, I touched the ends of the wires, triggering the detonator.

Attacked!

My explosion was the signal for Peter to set off his, and I heard the second explosion go off a mile down the track. Then both explosions were covered by the screeching sound of metal on metal and terrible crashes as the train began buckling, with each carriage piling into the back of the one in front.

Our men were already coming out of the jungle, guns aimed, firing at the flatbed trucks. There was very little need for any sustained attack; the explosives had done their work. The trucks and carriages and wagons had all turned over with the force of the crash, trapping Japanese soldiers under their weight.

It was all over in five minutes. The train wreckage spread along and across the track. Two of the carriages had been hurled into the jungle at the side with the force of it. Dead Japanese soldiers lay everywhere.

"Take the supplies from the wagons," ordered Captain Hayes. "Each man to carry what he can. Destroy the rest. Check our casualties."

As our soldiers disappeared back into the jungle, Peter, Cookie, Billy and I set to work rigging explosive charges to destroy the rest of the supplies that couldn't be carried. That done, we slipped back into the jungle and headed back to camp. We had struck our first major blow against the Japanese invaders.

After we'd destroyed the train and the railway line, we put as much distance as we could between ourselves and the scene of the ambush. To gain greater mileage, Major Rawns decided that, for once, we would use the road that ran through the jungle. It was a risky decision and one that Private Parker complained about bitterly as we marched at a fast pace.

"This is stupid," he grumbled. "Walking down a road. We could be walking right into a Jap camp. Or into a Jap convoy."

"Not half as big a risk as if he let us go slowly through the jungle," I responded. "They'd come down this road and cut us off before you could blink an eye. Think about it."

Parker thought about the consequences, and that silenced him.

There was no doubt that the Major was right to take the risk. After the destruction of the Japanese train, to say nothing of wrecking the supplies to the front-line troops and ruining the railway line itself, the Japanese would be searching for us with a vengeance. Speed was of the essence if we were to get away. Using this road we could travel at a fast march. We had a patrol at point, watching out for the enemy.

The other important factor about using this road was that we knew where we were on the map. Sometimes maps can be very misleading, especially when you're in the jungle. There are no particular markers and each swamp and each tree looks very much like every other swamp and tree.

We carried on marching right through the night, something else it's only possible to do on a road. Fortunately the moon was bright enough for us to see our path ahead.

I was worried that An Po wouldn't be able to keep up the pace, but I had underestimated her. Although she looked thin and underfed, she was very fit and strong. I guess it was the result of leading such a hard life in the jungle. Ba Maung also stayed beside her during the whole march as her protection.

Soon after dawn one of the runners came back from the point patrol. He looked as if he was about to collapse – he'd obviously run the half a mile from the patrol at a sprint speed, no mean task when fully laden with pack and rations.

"Jap convoy approaching!" he said. "Point patrol's taken cover."

"Right!" ordered Major Rawns. "Everyone into the jungle. And no one shoots unless we're spotted. Let them pass, understand. We'll make them think we haven't got this far yet."

Immediately all the men took cover in the jungle and put at least 200 yards between ourselves and the road.

We lay there in the bushes and low trees, guns hidden in the grass, but all pointing towards the road, ready to be used if necessary. We had only been lying there for about ten minutes when the first lorry of the Japanese convoy appeared, followed by more lorries and a couple of officers' cars. I guessed they were heading for the scene of the railway wreckage.

Although we could have ambushed the convoy with ease from our position hiding in the jungle, I felt Major Rawns showed great tactical skill in letting them pass. When they didn't come across us, the Japs would think we were escaping through the jungle and would put our estimated position at many miles further north than we were. If the Japs concentrated their search for us up there, then it would give us greater freedom of movement as we continued south to our next objective, the railway line between Mandalay and Lashio. But to get there we had another major obstacle to face, the wide and fast-moving Irrawaddy River.

For the next two days we moved south, keeping to the jungle. That fast march along the road had given us the advantage we needed. Now there was the danger that the road would lead us directly into Japanese hands, so we moved as fast as the jungle would allow, but keeping the road within two miles in case we needed it.

On the second day, one of the Burmese, Mek Ya, said that a village he knew was just four miles from our position. He had relatives there and felt that An Po would be safe there, if she agreed. An Po was keen to get back to her own people, so Mek Ya and Ba Maung went with her to the village while we continued our march through the jungle.

When Ba Maung and Mek Ya rejoined us some time later, Ba assured me that the villagers would take good care of An Po, and would say nothing about our presence, both from hatred, and from fear of reprisals against them from the Japanese.

During this time we received reports from Brigade HQ over the wireless letting us know about the progress of the other columns. Apparently our attack on the railway line had had a major effect on Japanese morale. Many ordinary Japanese soldiers were now afraid to sleep in camp at night in fear of the "round-eyed barbarians" who might sneak out of the jungle and attack them. As a result the Japanese High Command had decided that we must be caught to show the Japanese soldiery that we weren't some superhuman warriors, but ordinary men. The order had gone out that if we were caught we were to be interrogated for information about our comrades, and then we were to be killed. None of us were to be kept as prisoners.

"Death or glory, eh?" smiled Cookie when he heard this.

"No glory for us ordinary blokes," commented Parker acidly. "That's only for officers."

Another day's march through the jungle, and we came to our biggest obstacle so far: the Irrawaddy River. It was wider than the Chindwin and much faster flowing.

We set to work to cross it in the same way as we had the Chindwin. My small unit went over with the first of the rubber boats, our eyes scanning the opposite bank the whole time, guns ready for waiting Japanese. Once we had landed, we sent the boats back for the next wave, which brought the sappers. Meanwhile soldiers on both banks set to work cutting trees and making rafts. Working in relays this way we soon had about 150 men across with us on the southern bank of the river, including Captain Hayes, while Major Rawns stayed on the opposite bank directing operations.

The second wave of rafts were just setting off to cross the river, when suddenly the mules on the far bank began to make a peculiar braying sound. I looked across and saw the muleteers trying to calm them down, but even from this distance I could see that some of the mules had their ears back and their eyes were wide, nostrils flaring. The mules on the rafts were also twitchy and began to move about, making the rafts difficult to control. The mules on our side of the river caught the mood and began to bray and shift unhappily.

"Something's going on," whispered Cookie next to me. "Always trust an animal's sense of danger."

He slipped his gun off his shoulder and held it ready, aimed at the jungle ahead of us. His eyes scanned the dense trees for movement.

On the far bank the mules had calmed down, but only because the muleteers were talking to them, reassuring them. The second wave of rafts were now halfway across the river.

Suddenly there was a hail of gunfire from further up the Irrawaddy, catching all the men and mules who were in the middle of the river and mowing them down. The bullets also tore through the cable ropes, and the rafts were suddenly cut adrift. They began to hurtle downriver, bucking and tilting in the strong current, the bodies of our dead soldiers falling off the rafts into the river. The Japanese had found us!

Immediately, those of us on the south bank of the Irrawaddy turned our attention to firing at the attackers. The Japanese returned fire, bullets from their heavy guns smashing into the trees around us. Meanwhile, the rest of the Japanese attack force was closing in on Major Rawns and his men on the north bank. One by one they tumbled into the water, or fell dead in the mud. On our south bank we felt helpless. We couldn't fire at the troops attacking Major Rawns's position for fear of hitting our own men. We could only watch in horror as they were mown down.

Rawns turned to face us and shouted. Because of the noise of the gunfire we couldn't make out his words, but his gestures were clear. He was ordering Captain Hayes to move into the jungle, to get away as fast as possible.

I saw Hayes hesitate, loath to leave Rawns and his men, but he realized as surely as we all did that, stuck on this side as we were, there was nothing else to do. We all heard the bitterness and reluctance in Hayes's voice as he gave the order to move on into the jungle.

My last sight of Major Rawns and the men on the northern bank was of them firing into the jungle as they were cut down by heavy machine-gun fire. Major Rawns was among the last to fall. Then the jungle swallowed us up, and we saw no more. But fearful images of the day's events stayed with us for long afterwards.

Under Captain Hayes's command we pushed on as fast as we could, barely even stopping to rest. Most of our mules had been lost in the Japanese attack at the Irrawaddy. We now had only six mules for carrying our column's equipment. I immediately requisitioned two of the mules from Captain Hayes to carry the explosives. The wireless and its batteries were loaded on to the other four.

Of the original 400 men in our column who had set out across the Chindwin, we were now down to 150. We were a sombre bunch as we moved through the jungle, aware that we were now deep inside enemy territory with the Japanese sending the full weight of their army in pursuit of us.

We managed to radio for supplies, and sure enough they came the next day, parachuting down from the RAF supply plane. We didn't waste any time making camp once the drop had been carried out. We just gathered up the supplies, spread out the load with so much for each man to carry, and then set off as fast as we could through the jungle. We didn't doubt that the Japanese would have spotted the parachutes coming down and would be coming after us with all possible speed.

Over the next two days we came across signs of Japanese activity: deserted camps, reports of armed lorries, but we managed to keep ourselves away from actual contact with them. It was a life-or-death cat-and-mouse game being played out in the thick jungle: the Japanese looking for us in large numbers, and us keeping hidden as we continued on to our next objective, the railway line between Mandalay and Lashio.

The Japanese were so determined to catch us that they even did a leaflet drop, thousands of leaflets cascading down from their planes as they flew over the jungle. We managed to pick up a few that had blown our way with the wind. The leaflets were printed in three languages: English, Urdu and Burmese and their message was loud and clear:

To the Pitiable Anglo-Indian Soldiery.
Your forces have been utterly destroyed in the battle of the 3rd March, and not a man has been able to re-cross the Chindwin. The powerful Imperial Army of Nippon is all around you and you cannot possibly escape. Do not again trust your brutal and selfish British officers who will leave you to starve in the jungles as they did last year. Come to the nearest Nippon soldiers with this leaflet in your hand and we will treat you well.

I saw Private Parker reading one and gave him an icy stare. He screwed it up and threw it away, but there was no mistaking the thoughtful look on his face.

At our first chance to make a proper camp, I set out the map that showed the target railway line to the rest of my unit to discuss tactics. Private Parker made it clear that he wasn't keen on discussing any tactic except retreat.

"This is madness," he grumbled. "Over half of us dead, and it's just sheer luck that it wasn't all of us. We ought to head back."

"Where to?" I snapped. "Back into the hands of the Japanese?"

"They said in that leaflet we'd be treated well," he insisted.

"Yeah?" said Cookie sarcastically. "Like those four English soldiers we found in that village?"

Parker fell silent.

"Let's get this clear," I added. "We have a mission to accomplish. When that's done, or when we're given orders by Captain Hayes or Brigadier Wingate, then we head back. Not before."

I then turned back to the map.

"Right," I said. "Let's work out the best place to blow this thing."

Cookie, Billy, Ba and Tig joined me in studying the map. Parker wandered off to help put up a temporary hut.

Ba tapped the contour lines and indicated a spot where the jungle was shown as being particularly thick.

"Here is gorge," he said. "Not wide but very deep."

"How wide?" I asked.

Ba thought it over.

"Two hundred, maybe three hundred yards."

"Jungle on either side," mused Cookie.

"What's the bridge made of, Ba?" asked Billy. "Teak?"

"Teak and bamboo," nodded Ba. "Very strong."

"But very deep," I repeated thoughtfully. "The right charges placed in the correct place, the whole lot will come down. It would take the Japs months to rebuild a tall structure like that."

"Because it's so vulnerable it's bound to be well guarded," put in Billy. "Especially after the damage we did to the last railway line. There'll be Japs swarming all over it just waiting for us to show up."

I studied the map again, and then tapped another section of the railway line, about two miles away from the gorge. According to the map the line ran through jungle across the top of a plateau.

"This section of line won't be so well guarded," I pointed out.

"So?" said Cookie, slightly puzzled. "If we blow that section the Japs will be able to repair it in a few days. What's the point?"

“The point is a diversion,” I said. “We get Peter Simpson and his unit to set charges here while we make our way to the gorge. With a bit of luck the sound of the explosion when his charges go off will bring all the Japanese in the area rushing to the plateau, freeing the gorge for us to get at the bridge structure.”

“And what if the Japs decide to stay and guard the bridge instead?” asked Billy.

I shrugged, and forced a grin.

There was no need to answer; we all knew what would happen.

Into the Gorge

Three days later we made it to the railway line. Three days of hard travelling through treacherous jungle, battling with swamps, insects and illness. By now most of us were suffering from various jungle diseases and we were all feeling weak. With our diminishing rations we also had to conserve as much as possible because we didn't know when we'd be able to arrange another supply drop. We could have tried going into a local village and bartering for food, but Captain Hayes was against it for two reasons: the first was that it would put the villagers at risk; but the second and most tactical reason was that there might be someone in the village who'd report us to the Japanese for a reward.

Captain Hayes had accepted my recommendations for blowing the bridge at the gorge, with a diversion explosion on the nearby plateau. Peter Simpson was only too happy to take his unit and lay the explosion on the plateau. We agreed a time frame for the operation which would give him time to get clear, and my unit to get to the bridge. Our plan was for my unit to get to the top of the ridge overlooking the gorge. When we were there and ready to descend, we would signal to Peter by using mirrors. Peter would set his explosion to go off one hour after we'd signalled. By then, if we were lucky, we would be partway down the gorge. Providing the Japanese sent all their forces to investigate the explosion on the plateau, that would give us approximately an hour to get to the bridge structure and set our charges.

So at dawn on the morning of the third day, Cookie, Billy, Ba Maung, Tig Kyan, Private Parker and myself lay hidden in thick bushes at the ridge that looked down on to the gorge. We were about four miles from the bridge. I studied its approach tracks through my binoculars.

As we'd expected, the bridge was swarming with Japanese soldiers, patrolling the railway line that ran across it.

I moved the binoculars down to the bed of the gorge itself. The structure that held up the bridge was guarded by about twenty Japanese soldiers. The Japs had obviously reached the same conclusion as we had: the gorge was the most vulnerable place for the railway line to be attacked.

Cookie had also been scanning the floor of the gorge with his binoculars.

"I've counted twenty-three soldiers down there," he said.

"I made it twenty," I said.

"I spotted a few more hiding in the bushes," he said. "They've also got a machine-gun post down there. I can guarantee they won't be moving from their spot, so we'll have to deal with them."

"Twenty-three against five," murmured Billy. "That's not too bad."

"That's without the ones on the bridge," I pointed out. "I've counted another twenty-five up top."

"Fifty against five," nodded Billy. "Ten against one. Now those are the sort of odds that make it interesting."

I took out my mirror and flashed it into the sun twice, sending my message to Peter on the plateau that we were ready. At first there was no answering flash, and I wondered if Peter and his unit had actually made it safely to the plateau or if they'd been caught before they got there. There hadn't been any sounds of firing from that direction, and Captain Hayes had decided that most of the supporting soldiers would give Peter cover. That way there was less chance of our smaller unit being spotted. I was just about to flash my mirror again, when I saw Peter's answer as his mirror caught the sun's rays. He was ready.

"OK," I said. "Let's go."

So we began our descent down the side of the gorge to the jungle floor below. Luckily, the sides of the gorge were covered in thick jungle, so we were able to keep under cover the whole time. It was an arduous journey hauling the explosives down into the gorge, especially because we were weak from illness and meagre rations. I kept one eye on my watch the whole time, ticking off the minutes. We needed to get to the bottom of the gorge just as Peter's explosion went off. We had to strike while the Japanese were momentarily off guard, distracted by the first explosion. Any delay and we would get caught by them when they returned, once they'd discovered the first explosion hadn't caused major damage. We were still about half a mile from the floor of the gorge when we heard the explosion from the plateau.

By the sound of it, Peter had done a good job. A loud explosion guaranteed to attract attention. We heard shouts and yells from the soldiers on the bridge, and from those down in the gorge itself. We also heard some firing coming from the soldiers guarding the approaches to the bridge.

Billy scanned the bridge through his binoculars and whispered: "It's working! They're all heading for the plateau!"

"All of them?" I asked.

Billy looked again.

"They've left the machine-gun crew," he reported. "Two men. Plus I think I can see another one walking around down there." He looked through his binoculars again and nodded. "Yes, definitely three of them."

"Me, Ba Maung and Tig Kyan will take care of them," said Cookie.

I nodded. "No shooting, though," I said. "Silently. We can't risk anything that will attract attention and bring the other Japs back too soon."

"No worries," said Cookie grimly.

"Right. In that case, Billy, Parker, you two carry the explosives and stay with me," I said. "We'll let Cookie, Ba and Tig take out the guards first. Then we'll go to work. Cookie, Ba and Tig, you keep watch while we're busy."

They all nodded. I took a deep breath. What was it Cookie had said? That this was death or glory? Well, our moment of death or glory was upon us now.

Ready to Blow

We crept through the jungle floor of the gorge. Above us on the plateau about two miles away we could hear the sounds of shouting and occasionally shots being fired. Peter's blowing of the railway line had caused the diversion that we needed.

When we were within fifty yards of the bridge, I gestured for Billy and Parker to stay with me while Cookie, Ba Maung and Tig Kyan went ahead to deal with the guards.

Cookie and the two Burmese slipped into the bushes ahead and disappeared. Billy, Parker and I crouched, straining our ears. We could hear the Japanese chatting. They obviously thought all the danger was up on the plateau where the other troops were. Suddenly the chatting stopped. We heard grunts, choking sounds, and then silence. Then a quiet low whistle, like a bird. Cookie was telling us everything was clear.

Billy, Parker and I moved forward and reached the base of the bridge where the tangle of support beams were sunk into the ground. Cookie, Ba Maung and Tig Kyan were already stripping the jackets and caps from the dead soldiers and putting them on. That done, they dragged the dead bodies into the undergrowth. Then they took their positions at the machine gun. Anyone glancing down from the plateau would see what looked like the same Japanese crew.

I stationed Parker in the jungle to keep watch in case anyone should approach. Also, I didn't want him working with me while I laid the charges. Parker was very nervous, and letting a nervous man handle explosives could have been fatal for all of us. Billy and I set to work, climbing up the middle support to the crucial joining section.

I set a primary charge which could be activated instantly if we were suddenly interrupted. The problem was, it would also blow us up with it. When that was set, Billy and I stuck the plastic explosive at crucial points along the middle section. Then we ran the wires into them. That done, we set the timer pencils. I used three lots of timer pencils set to go off at five-minute intervals. This was partly a precaution in case one of the timer pencils should fail, and also it added to the overall damage when there was one explosion on top of another. I set the first charge to go off in 45 minutes.

As soon as the charges were set, Billy and I clambered back down the wooden bridge supports as fast as we could.

"Let's go!" I whispered to Cookie, Ba and Tig. They grabbed up their own jackets and followed us into the jungle. As we moved, they tore off their Japanese uniforms and put their own back on. It was a wise move – they didn't fancy being shot accidentally by our own boys.

We found Private Parker where we'd left him. "I think the Japs are coming back down," he whispered, fear in his eyes.

I looked up at the plateau through my binoculars. Parker was right. A detachment of Japanese soldiers was already heading back down into the gorge. I wondered whether we'd been spotted, or if someone had just noticed that the machine-gun crew had suddenly vanished. Whatever the reason, I calculated that it would take them just over half an hour to get down into the gorge. That would give them time to spot the explosives charges, and dismantle them.

"I'm going back to reset the timers," I said.

Cookie stopped me. "You'll never make it," he said. "By the time you get up there the Japs will be nearly down. They'll get you easily before you have a chance to get away."

"I'm not going to get away," I said grimly. "I'll set the charges to go up instantly."

"That's madness!" said Billy. "You'll be blown up yourself!"

"At least the bridge will be gone," I said.

"I'm not going to let you do it," said Cookie.

"Cookie, I'm going to pull rank on you," I said. "I'm in charge of this unit and those are my orders."

"Forget it, Lieutenant," said Cookie firmly. "Make one move towards that bridge and I'll knock you out."

"And you can count me in on that," added Billy. "Anyway,

there's a way we can still blow the bridge with a good chance of us getting away without you killing yourself."

"How?" I asked.

"We hold them down in the gorge," answered Billy. "Stop them getting up the bridge to the detonators."

"But we'll be killed!" protested Parker. "Look how many of them there are! We're outnumbered!"

I looked at the bridge and weighed up what Billy had suggested. It was possible. If we could keep them pinned down just long enough to blow the bridge, it might just work. Our only hope was that they would think we were a bigger unit than we were. If they realized there were just six of us they'd launch a full-scale attack on our position, while others disarmed the detonators. If that happened, then Parker would be right. We'd be overwhelmed, and they wouldn't be taking us prisoner. However, it was the best hope we had of blowing up the bridge.

"OK." I nodded. "That's what we'll do. Spread out so that once we start firing they'll think they're surrounded by a big unit."

"This is madness!" protested Parker.

"Maybe, but it's our only option," I said. "Get to your positions. Hold your fire until I open up. The longer we can leave it until we let them know we're here, the better it'll be for us."

We spread out across the floor of the gorge, each of us finding a hiding place in the thick bush. I focused my binoculars on the Japanese soldiers working their way down the side of the gorge. There were seventeen of them. The others had obviously stayed to guard the broken railway line. I looked at my watch. There were now just fifteen minutes to go before the first charge went off. I looked at the Japanese soldiers. The first one was stepping down on to the floor the gorge. Then the next. Then another. It would only be a matter of seconds before they spotted that the soldiers who should have been guarding the machine gun were gone, and all hell would then be let loose.

Splitting Up

There was a cry of alarm from one of the Japanese soldiers. As I guessed, he'd spotted that the comrades they'd left in the gorge were missing. His yell brought the other soldiers running, the rest of them scrambling down the side of the gorge, guns levelled and ready. It only took them a few minutes to find the bodies of their three dead comrades. In my hiding place I checked my watch. The first charge was due to go off in twelve minutes. Twelve long, agonizing minutes to wait.

The soldiers spent another two minutes examining the bodies and talking excitedly in Japanese as they tried to work out what had happened, then one who was a junior officer of sorts snapped out a command and they all shut up.

The officer began pacing around the machine gun, checking for tracks. All this took another two minutes. Eight minutes before blast-off.

Suddenly one of the other soldiers, who had been gazing around, looked up at the bridge supports, and yelled out. The officer and the rest of the Japanese soldiers looked up at where he was pointing, and spotted the plastic explosive and the charges.

Immediately there was a state of panic, which was only brought under control by the officer. He pointed up at the explosives, ordering one of the soldiers to climb up and disarm them. I checked my watch. Six minutes to go.

The soldier looked unwilling to carry out this task, but he was a good soldier who obeyed orders, and he began to climb up. I let him get six feet off the ground, and then I opened fire with my Thompson, as did the others. He was hit on the leg, lost his balance and fell to the ground.

The rest of the Japanese soldiers took cover in the bushes. Then they opened up with returning fire.

I took a glance up towards the plateau. The shooting down in the gorge had attracted the attention of the other Japanese, and even as I watched I could see them starting to return.

Four minutes to go. That was provided the timer pencils worked.

The Japanese officer shouted an order, and some of his men began to work their way towards us. A hail of bullets from our positions in the bushes sent them scurrying back, although two of them fell to the ground where they stood.

The soldiers descending the side of the gorge increased their pace. If they reached the bottom before the charges went off, we'd be overwhelmed by them.

I fired off another machine-gun burst at the bridge. Two minutes to go.

Another man was now climbing up, then a second. They were making a massive effort to get up and disable the explosives. Meanwhile, their comrades were now keeping rapid fire on our positions, making it difficult for us to get any proper aim on the two climbing soldiers.

One minute to go.

One of the soldiers was now only about four feet away from the first charge.

Zero ... but nothing happened! The first timer didn't go off! That meant another five minutes before the second timer pencil detonated its charge. Five precious minutes!

The climbing soldier inched towards the explosive, his hand clawing upwards towards the detonator wire. In a few seconds more he would be there.

Suddenly the delayed first charge went off. The soldier and the wooden support strut he was on disappeared in a burst of flame and smoke.

"That's it!" I yelled. "Out!"

While the Japanese soldiers looked up in horror at the bridge above them as it creaked and swayed, we began to retreat.

We headed along the gorge, away from the now tottering bridge. As we ran I heard another explosion behind us as the second timer went off. I turned. The wooden supports had broken and were falling down into the gorge like so much firewood, some of them still burning. Above them the railway bridge itself, no longer supported, was swaying like a length of twisted ribbon in the wind. And then the whole structure collapsed, tumbling down into the gorge and sending dust and smoke rising high into the air. The bridge and the Japanese soldiers disappeared completely as thick clouds of smoke and dust poured towards us along the floor of the gorge.

I didn't stop to watch any more. I rushed to join Cookie and the others, heading up the steep side of the gorge. With a bit of luck the Japanese would be too occupied with the collapsing bridge to worry about giving chase to us immediately. Our mission was accomplished.

We made it back through the jungle to where Captain Hayes and the rest of our column were waiting for us. Reports of our success in blowing up the bridge had already got back, and they greeted us with handshakes and hearty slaps on the back. I sought out Peter Simpson and congratulated him and his crew on their work in creating the diversionary explosion blowing up the railway line.

"Yes, but you got the big one," grinned Peter. "I watched it from cover. A beautiful piece of work!"

Captain Hayes joined us.

"When you two have finished congratulating each other,"

he said. “We’ve got orders from Brigade Command. Now the bridge is blown, our mission’s over. Brigade Command have ordered us to head back to our own lines. Our orders are to split the command up into small units. With the Japs combing the jungle for us, a big column is bound to be spotted.” Hayes turned and looked at us. “That’s it, chaps. Small units, and I’m afraid the only supplies are those you have with you right now. They can’t chance another drop. So, do your best not to get caught. And, with a bit of luck, we’ll see each other back in India.”

I turned and caught Billy’s look. He looked the same as I did. The feeling of achievement and exultation over blowing the bridge had gone. Now there was just the reality. Hundreds of miles through the jungle to get back to our own lines. Declining rations. No ammo. Weak from jungle sicknesses. And between us and our home base was the Japanese army, 80,000 strong, all with express orders to find us, and kill us.

Homeward Bound

For the first time in this jungle campaign I was now completely responsible for the men of my small unit: Cookie, Billy, Ba Maung, Tig Kyan and Private Parker. I decided on a democratic approach to our withdrawal. I may have been the expert when it came to blowing things up, but Cookie and Billy were more experienced jungle hands than me, and Ba Maung and Tig Kyan even more so in this particular jungle. As the rest of our column dispersed into the jungle, I sat down, unfolded my map, and held a council of war with my men.

"Right," I said. "As officer in charge I'll take any final decisions, but as all our lives are at risk, and you chaps know about the jungle better than me, I want your suggestions as to how we can get out of here quickly and safely."

Cookie, Billy, Ba and Tig studied the map. Private Parker hung about on the edge of the clearing, nervous, his Lee Enfield rifle held ready, expecting the Japanese to attack us at any moment.

I traced two routes on the map with my finger.

"The shortest route is due west, back across the Irrawaddy, and then strike north-west up to the southern part of the

Indian border. The longer route is due north up into China. Whichever route we take we have to cross the Chindwin."

"The Japs are bound to be watching the Irrawaddy," said Cookie. "Getting across where the river's wide is going to be difficult. We don't have any boats ourselves so we're going to have to commandeer some from a village, which will put both us and the villagers at risk. Word will also get back to the Japanese, letting them know our position."

"On the other hand, if we head north and cross the Irrawaddy where it's just a stream, it will add days to our journey," Billy pointed out. "And we don't have the rations."

"What about living off the jungle?" I asked, looking at Cookie.

Cookie laughed. "Yes and no," he said. "We can get some food from the jungle as we move, but not in bulk. Not for six of us."

"So long as we can find enough to give us the strength to keep moving," I said.

We pored over the map for another ten minutes, with suggestions being made by Ba and Tig about the different kinds of jungle we would be passing through in both directions. Finally, after weighing all the pros and cons up, I made my decision.

"The logical choice, if we had sufficient rations, would be to strike north and head for China, avoiding the Irrawaddy.

The Japs don't know we're short of food, so my guess is that's the way they think we'll be heading. So, instead we head due west."

"Straight into where the enemy are watching for us?!" gasped Parker in horror.

I shrugged. "The enemy are watching for us everywhere," I said. "I'm hoping that we can catch them by surprise. They won't think anyone would be so foolish as to try and cross the Irrawaddy after what happened to us last time. Once we're across—"

"If we get across," grumbled Parker.

"Once we're across," I repeated firmly, with a glare at Parker that silenced him, "we head along here, taking the shortest route to the Chindwin. Split up as we are, we've got a very good chance of making it, because with a bit of luck the Japanese won't be able to cope with chasing so many units."

Cookie gave another grin. "Always the optimist," he laughed. "What happens if we get the bad luck and all the Japs suddenly come after *us*?!"

"In that case we'll be outnumbered about 80,000 to six." I grinned back. "And we'll be running so fast we won't have time to worry about it." I folded the map up and put it in my pack. "Right," I said, "let's get going. We've got 300 miles of hard travelling."

And so we began our journey back. I decided to try another bold tactic, one which had worked successfully after we'd ambushed the train, and which I hoped the Japanese would think of as too lunatic and dangerous for us to try: I used the road. However, to cut down our chances of being caught by the Japanese, we marched at night.

My thinking on this was that we would see the headlights of any approaching Japanese trucks in the dark, and so could take cover.

Travelling by night also gave us further protection: in the dark, it would be difficult for any Japanese patrols to spot us as the enemy. Unable to identify our uniforms, I hoped they would assume that any body of men marching boldly along a road couldn't possibly be British.

In this way, travelling along the road by night and hiding under cover in the jungle during the day, we made good time, and three days later we were within twenty miles of the Irrawaddy without once having come face to face with any Japanese.

We'd been aware of them, though. A couple of times while hiding in the jungle we'd smelt the smoke from fires, which could have meant a Japanese camp not far away. With our declining rations, the temptation to attack the camp and take some food had been hard to resist, but we tightened our belts and stayed under cover.

We'd also heard some shooting and guessed that the Japanese had stumbled on to some of our men making their escape. I could only hope that they had made it.

The last stretch to the Irrawaddy was through thick jungle, and we stumbled and squelched through swamp much of the time, our guns held above our heads to keep them dry. The trees seemed to close in on us all the time and we had to hack our way through many miles, the muscles of our arms sore and aching with swinging our machetes, cutting a path through the thick undergrowth that blocked our way.

After hours of this, with darkness starting to fall, we came to the edge of the jungle where the mudbank ran down to the Irrawaddy. Here the river was wide and fast flowing, too wide and with too strong a current for us to try to swim across.

We worked our way along the bank of the river, keeping to the cover of the jungle the whole time, looking for a place where the river might be narrower, a boat might have been left moored, or where a stretch of sandbank might give us a start to cross. We trekked cautiously through the jungle for two miles, our eyes on the river but our ears alert for any sounds of enemy troops in the jungle, and taking turns on point.

I was taking my turn at second point just behind Cookie,

when he stopped and raised a hand. I crept forward to join him. We peered through the trees. There at the river's edge were two huts made of bamboo, with thatched roofs. And flying above them was a Japanese flag. From inside, we could hear voices.

The River

Billy, Ba Maung, Tig Kyan and Parker had now caught up with Cookie and me. The six of us crouched in the jungle and surveyed the huts ahead of us. I could see four armed Japanese soldiers on guard duty, one at each side of the bamboo landing stage on the river, and another two stationed nearer to the jungle. I guessed there would be at least another four soldiers inside the huts, maybe more.

I looked through my binoculars at the opposite bank, scanning the trees, and motioned Billy and Cookie to do the same.

"Well?" I whispered.

"There's another small encampment on the opposite bank, hidden just inside the trees," said Billy, keeping his voice low.

"That's what I saw." I nodded. "From the number of huts I can make out, I doubt if there are more than eight Japanese on that side of the river."

"Ten," said Cookie, who was still scanning the far bank through his binoculars. "I can see them."

"So, ten on that bank, about the same number on this," I calculated.

"And a boat," said Billy, pointing.

We all looked harder. We could just see the end of a boat, a small flat pontoon, the bulk of it hidden behind the huts.

"It doesn't look much," commented Parker.

"Right at this moment, anything bigger than a rubber duck is better than nothing," Billy told him.

I eased further back in the trees and then moved along the bank so I could get a better view of the pontoon.

"It's large enough to take us," I said.

"Where, straight into the Japs on the other side?" asked Parker acidly.

"No, downriver," I said.

"Down?" queried Cookie. "I thought we were trying to head north?"

"Do you fancy trying to paddle against the current while those Japs on the other bank are shooting at us?" I asked him.

Cookie saw what I was getting at, and grinned ruefully. "Point taken, boss," he said.

My plan was to snatch the boat and use the current to take us downriver at speed, letting the river carry us while we kept our hands free to fire at the Japs on the other bank. Once we were a safe distance downstream, then we'd head into the opposite bank. But first we had to get hold of the boat. And to do that we had to get past the Japanese.

I gave my orders in a whisper, and then we set off through the jungle, heading towards the bamboo huts.

Fortunately for us, the guards on duty had got complacent. I suppose they didn't think that anyone would try anything so foolish as to attempt to cross a river where there was a fortified Japanese post.

Cookie and Ba Maung crept through the jungle right up to where it became mud. Billy and I kept our tommy guns trained on the two guards, just in case anything should go wrong.

Our two disappeared from our sight, taking cover behind thick bushes near the bamboo huts.

The guards made their patrol, their route taking them right by the bushes where Cookie and Ba Maung were hiding.

They struck in a flash, both leaping up from their cover and pulling the two guards down behind the bushes. There was hardly a sound. Then Cookie appeared from behind the bushes and gave me a thumbs-up sign.

I motioned Billy, Tig and Parker to follow me, and we crept through the jungle to join Cookie and Ba Maung near the huts. The two guards on duty on the landing stage hadn't heard a thing; they were still standing on the rough bamboo platform, looking up and down the river.

I gave my orders in a low whisper: "Billy and Parker, you

take the first hut. Cookie and Tig, you take the other. Ba and I will take out the guards on the river."

I did a countdown on my upheld fingers to give them their cue: three – two – one...

As one we sprang up and moved. Billy kicked in the door of the first hut and leapt in, his gun already blazing, and Cookie did the same to the second hut, the sound of their guns tearing into the jungle stillness.

Ba Maung and I were already running past the huts, our guns firing as the two Japanese soldiers on guard duty looked at us in surprise.

The noise of our attack had already roused the soldiers on the far bank and I could see them pouring out of the jungle towards the river, guns at the ready.

Cookie, Billy, Parker and Tig had now joined us on the landing stage.

"Into the boat!" I ordered.

I hardly needed to say it. Billy was already untying the rope that held the boat to the post. A few seconds later we were on our way, the boat rocking and turning, caught in the fast current of the river, while we kept firing at the Japanese on the opposite bank.

The soldiers on the far side of the river were now running along the mudflat, trying to keep up with us. A hail of bullets ripped into the boat, tearing off splinters of wood and metal.

Suddenly the craft lurched violently. It had clipped a rock. Ba and Tig fought to get it back under control before it capsized completely. Then I heard a yell behind me, and I turned, just in time to see Parker topple out of the boat and into the water with an expression of horror on his face, and he clutched desperately for help as the current swept him away.

Casualties of War

"Cover me!" I shouted to the others.

I grabbed the rope that was still tied round the end of the small boat, and jumped into the river.

Luckily, Parker had fallen off the boat away from the bank where the Japanese soldiers were firing at us, so it offered us some protection. Cookie, Billy, Ba Maung and Tig Kyan maintained fire into the jungle, doing their best to keep the Japs down.

I swam towards Parker as fast as I could and just managed to catch up with him as he went down. He bobbed back to the surface, gasping desperately for air.

"Here!" I yelled, and thrust the rope towards him.

Parker grabbed the rope with one hand and then disappeared under the surface of the water again.

"Haul him in!" I shouted at the boat.

Ba Maung was on it already, pulling on the rope while Cookie, Billy and Tig kept up covering fire.

I dived under the surface and felt the fast-moving current drag me down and around. Reaching out I felt my hands touch Parker's clothes. I gripped him and kicked back to the surface again. With one hand under his chin, I held his head above the water as Ba pulled him in.

By now Tig was using a paddle he'd found in the boat to take us towards the far bank.

Ba reached down and grabbed Parker by the collar and held him half-out of the water as the boat headed into the shallows of the mudbank. I hauled myself up on to the edge of the boat and let myself be dragged along with it. The current had carried us quite a distance. The Japanese soldiers were still coming after us though; we could hear them crashing through the jungle towards our position.

The boat slid into the bank and ran aground.

"Out!" I yelled.

Cookie, Billy and Tig leapt on to the bank and ran into the jungle to defend our position, while Ba Maung and I dragged the half-conscious Parker out of the water and hauled him across the mud to the grass where the bank became jungle again.

"Here they come!" yelled Billy.

The Japanese soldiers came into view through the trees, their guns blazing bullets towards us. Cookie, Billy and Tig were already firing back. Ba and I dropped Parker face down on to the ground. While Ba snatched his gun and joined the fight, I worked on Parker, pressing on his back and pushing the water out of his lungs until he began to cough and splutter.

Reassured that Parker was alive and would recover, I turned and ran back towards the boat, squelching through the mud as I ran. Having retrieved my tommy gun I returned to the battle. The fire from the Japanese hidden in the trees was dying down. We were winning.

And then suddenly I saw Billy fall, and his gun dropped to the ground.

I let fly with a long burst, as did the others, and the shooting from the Japs stopped.

While Ba, Tig and I moved forward, guns at the ready, into the trees, Cookie went to check on Billy.

Six Japanese soldiers lay dead in the jungle. That meant the others had stayed back at their camp and were even now radioing our position to their unit.

I hurried back to see how Billy was.

Cookie was kneeling over him. Billy didn't move, he just lay there, a pool of blood staining the grass beneath him.

As I got there Cookie stood up, shook his head, a look of deep pain on his young face.

"Billy took a hit in the neck." He paused, then added: "He's dead."

Trapped

Cookie and I looked down at our comrade. This boy of nineteen had come all the way from Kenya to fight for his home country, and now he had died out here in the jungle of south-east Asia. I felt a deep sense of sadness and loss. I'd lost friends before in this war, but Cookie, Billy and I had been together since we'd first started our commando training the year before. But there was no time to dwell any further.

"Take his rations, weapons and ammo," I said. "We have to move on fast. Jap reinforcements will be on their way."

While Cookie took Billy's equipment I went to see how Parker was doing.

The private was on his feet, still coughing and soaked to the skin.

"We have to move on," I said.

"I understand, sir," he said.

I was a little surprised by his attitude, expecting a complaint of some sort from him about nearly drowning. I was even more amazed when he held out his hand to me.

"Thank you, sir," he said. "You saved my life. I didn't think you would. Don't you lot just leave your blokes behind if anything happens to them?"

I took his hand and shook it.

"Not if there's a chance to save someone," I said.

I let his hand go and gestured at Billy.

"I'm afraid not everyone can be saved," I said sadly.

Parker looked at Billy, and nodded.

"I'm sorry," he replied. "I know he was your pal."

"He was," I said. I felt too choked up with emotion to say all the things that I wanted to say.

Cookie had now distributed Billy's belongings between himself, Ba Maung and Tig Kyan. "Ready," he told me.

"OK," I said. "Let's move on!"

We spent the next days on the move, stopping only to snatch a few hours' sleep in deep cover in the jungle when we could, taking turns to keep watch.

I guessed that the Japanese would expect us to head due west, or else head north, and that's where they'd concentrate their search for us. Instead, as soon as we left the scene of the gun battle with the Japanese on the bank of the Irrawaddy, we took a diversionary route south along the river for ten miles before heading west. It added more time to our journey and made a greater demand on our few declining precious rations, but I hoped it would avoid us running into another large Japanese patrol.

By now we were all getting thinner and weaker. We were driving ourselves on through adrenaline and a sheer sense of determination to get back to our own lines. No longer in wireless contact we had no idea how the rest of our brigade were doing – if any of them had made it back yet, or if they'd been caught. All we could do was hack our way through the jungle, battling with swamps and insects, and doing our best to be as quiet as possible as we made our way. By now our map was useless, we were so far off any track, my compass and the sun were our only guides to the direction we were heading.

After six days of taking an erratic course in this way, doubling back on ourselves and laying false trails to throw any pursuer off our scent, we finally made it to the Chindwin. Only this time the river was heavily patrolled by Japanese.

We crouched in the jungle and I surveyed the nearest bank of the river through my binoculars. There were bamboo huts, with broad-leaf roofs, dotted at intervals along the riverbank. Japanese patrols covered the area, armed soldiers marching up and down along the bank between each hut. Machine-gun posts had been set up at intervals. This was no longer just open jungle leading to the river; this was a fortified front line. After the attacks we'd made on them behind their own lines, the Japanese had thrown a net along the whole length of the Chindwin, determined to catch as many of our Chindit brigade as they could in revenge.

And right now we were caught in that net. We couldn't go forward, and we couldn't go back. It was a bitter feeling to have come so far, to be so near to our own lines, and yet at the same time be so far away.

"Any ideas?" asked Cookie.

"Our only hope is that our own troops are watching on the other side of the river," I said. "If we can get part of the way across they might be able to give us covering fire."

"It's a big 'if'," said Cookie. "We've been out of contact for so long we don't know what the situation is. For all we know the Japs may have taken both sides of the river."

Reluctantly, I had to admit that Cookie could well be right. If they were, then we were well and truly sunk. Even if we made it to the Chindwin and managed to get partway across, the Japs on the other side would mow us down in mid-river.

"I'm afraid it's a chance we're going to have to take," I said. "We can't go back, and we're certainly not going to surrender. Remember, the Japs have orders to kill any of us they catch."

"So we go across," nodded Cookie. "Where?"

"I guess we have to look for the weak spot in the net," I said.

We spent the rest of that day crawling through the jungle, keeping parallel to the Chindwin, looking for a gap that we could make a dash through and get to the river. We didn't find one. The Japanese had learnt from their previous encounters with us at both the Chindwin and the Irrawaddy and had closed it up tight. Our other problem was that, even if we did make it to the river, we didn't have any way of getting across except by swimming. And swimming across the Chindwin with its dangerous undercurrents could be fatal – we all risked being sucked under and drowned.

Early the next morning, as dawn broke, we were still working our way slowly through the jungle, within distant sight of the Chindwin, searching for a place to make our escape. It was Tig Kyan who first spotted what might give us a slim chance. A number of logs had been felled at the edge of the jungle in readiness for building more patrol huts. They had fallen so that their tops lay right at the edge of the river, almost into the water.

"There," said Tig. "We use logs as boats."

"We'll never get them into the water without the soldiers seeing us," said Parker doubtfully. "Just look at the length of them. We're talking very heavy logs. It'd take all five of us just to push one."

"The mud will help us," I said. "They'll slide."

"On the other hand, they might just sink into the mud and stick," said Cookie.

"And we'll be sitting ducks," I admitted. "But those logs are the only chance we've got to get across that river."

We studied the scene. A Japanese patrol guarded the area where the fallen logs lay. Another patrol of seven soldiers was stationed a further hundred yards upriver by one of the bamboo huts, with yet another patrol the same distance downriver from the logs.

"We need a diversion," Cookie said. "Something to attract their attention while we get to the logs."

I thought it over, then I announced.

"I'll blow up the hut."

"You'll never get near enough to plant your charges," pointed out Cookie. "Anyway, we've got no plastic explosive left."

"I'll do it the old-fashioned way," I said, and produced a hand grenade from my pack.

"We've got four of these left between us. I'll throw three of them at one-minute intervals at the hut. The first should bring the Japs by the logs running. The second should keep them down, wondering where the next attack is coming from. I'll let drop my third one into the hut while you, Cookie, chuck our last grenade at the Jap patrol downriver at the same time. Once the grenades have gone off, Cookie and I will just keep firing at the Japs to keep them down.

"While all this is going on, Parker, Ba Maung and Tig Kyan, you get yourselves ready near the bank. As the last grenades go off, push one of the logs into the river and start kicking with it. Cookie and I will join you, so you'd better choose one big enough to take the weight of all five of us."

"Not that any of us weigh that much any more," laughed Cookie.

"When do we move?" asked Tig.

"We wait until dark," I said. "No sense in letting the Japs have clear aim at us in daylight."

"If one of us loses his grip on the log in the river in the dark, we won't be able to see him to save him," Cookie pointed out.

I shrugged. "True," I said, "but this is our only option. So we'll just have to hang on as tightly as we can, and kick hard towards the opposite bank."

"And hope we're not swimming right into Japanese hands," said Parker gloomily.

Back Across the Chindwin

We stayed hidden in the jungle until darkness fell. I spent the time planning my path through the trees so that I could get near enough to the hut to lob the grenades. Once I'd done that, I knew I then had the difficult task of getting out of the jungle, along the top of the mudbank, and joining up with Parker, Ba Maung and Tig Kyan as they pushed the log into the river. There were so many things that could go wrong. The log could stick and sink in the mud. The grenades might have got damaged on our trip. The moon might suddenly come out from behind cloud and light us up as if it was broad daylight. Or it might be so dark that we miss each other. My only hope was that Cookie and I would cause so much confusion with our grenades and gunfire that the Japs would be running around in panic thinking they were under attack from the jungle and not realize what was actually going on.

Two hours later, darkness fell.

We could just see one or two of the soldiers still standing at the river's edge. Most of the other guards upriver had retreated to the hut, and those downriver had gathered round a small fire. The fire sent out a glow, which would help them to spot us. But on the other hand, if Cookie was able to place his grenade close enough to the fire to blow the burning embers over the soldiers, it would cause even more panic and confusion. I suggested this to him, and he nodded.

"It's going to be difficult, though," I said. "You'll have to get pretty near for it to be accurate."

"No worries," he said. "You should have seen me playing cricket back in Oz. I was a devil in the outfield. I could hit the stumps from a hundred yards."

"Let's hope your aim's still as good," I grinned. "OK, Parker, Ba and Tig, work your way down towards the river. As soon as the action goes off, run for the river. And once you get that log afloat, start kicking water. Don't wait for us." I grimaced ruefully. "And just in case we don't make it, good luck. You've been a great bunch of blokes to work with. The best."

With that, Cookie and I headed off towards our own separate targets, while Parker, Ba Maung and Tig Kyan made their own way to the water's edge.

As I crept through the trees my mind went back to my first jungle training exercise when Sergeant Ross had caught me out. I remembered what I had learnt that night from him, and from many other nights afterwards. Merge with the jungle. Be part of it. Be an extension of the trees, the bushes, the mud, the air. Move like an animal does when it's stalking its prey, slowly, all senses alert, but silent, invisible.

I crept nearer and nearer to the hut. There were faint ripples on the surface of the river as the clouds broke enough for moonlight to shine through. Then the clouds covered the moon and it was dark again.

I was within throwing distance now. My first throw had to be accurate. I had to make sure it went between the trees and into the hut. The last thing I wanted was for the grenade to hit a branch and bounce back towards me.

Through the gloom I could make out the shape of one of the guards, strolling away from the hut, continuing his patrol. I took my first grenade, pulled out the pin, counted down … and then threw it. It careered through the trees and landed just beside the hut with a soft thud. The sentry turned. As he headed back towards the hut, the grenade went off.

Immediately, there was panic and confusion, yell and shouts from inside the hut as the bamboo caught fire. Soldiers stumbled out on to the mudbank, grabbing up their weapons. I counted down the seconds … 20 … 15 … 10… Just as the chaos and panic was starting to get under control, I lobbed my second grenade, this one hurling some of the soldiers back into the jungle.

Already the Japanese from downriver were running towards the spot, yelling and shouting, guns all over the place as they looked for any sign of the attackers.

I lobbed my third grenade right into the crowd of

soldiers now gathered around the burning hut, and it went off with devastating effect. At the same time I heard the explosion further downriver as Cookie's grenade exploded. Then I began my run towards where I hoped that Parker, Ba and Tig had managed to get the log into the water.

I squelched through the mud towards the river, sinking as I ran. I could just make out the figures of Parker, Ba Maung and Tig Kyan up to their waists in water, pushing the log away from the bank. Cookie was with them. I was just about to make it into the water when a sudden pain tore through my right leg and I went down. Behind me the yelling and firing continued, bullets tearing into the ground around me.

I tried to get to my feet, but my right leg was broken below the knee and I just sank back down again, an incredible pain shooting right up through my body. Then another bullet thudded into my shoulder, knocking me flat into the mud. My tommy gun jumped out of my hands. Frantically I reached out for it, but it was too far away. Footsteps were approaching me now, the splash of heavy boots in mud. All I could do was wait and be killed. Then a figure loomed over me.

"Come on, Lieutenant," said Parker. "The last boat is waiting."

"Go on without me!" I shouted. "That's an order!"

"You can court-martial me when we get home," answered Parker.

He dragged me along the mud, towards the river. The pain in my right leg and left shoulder as he hauled me along was incredible. Then I felt the water lapping around me as we waded into the Chindwin.

As we arrived at the log, I saw the figure of Cookie standing waist-deep in the water, tommy gun levelled, and he let off a long burst of fire.

"That should keep them busy!" he snapped.

I bumped against the floating log, and reached up with my one good arm to grab on to part of a cut-off branch that was protruding out.

Cookie and Parker hauled themselves half-out of the water on to the log, lying flat across it, while keeping a grip on my uniform, helping to hold me steady.

"Kick!" yelled Cookie.

Behind us the firing continued. Bullets fizzed into the water around us, now and then one thudding into the log, but it was too dark and we were moving too fast with the current for them to get a clear shot.

When we were over halfway across I wondered if more Japanese were waiting for us on the other side. Suddenly our worst fears were realized because, as we neared the opposite bank, gunfire opened up from the trees.

"We're finished!" yelled Parker.

"No!" shouted Cookie. "They're not shooting at us! They're our blokes giving us covering fire!"

The pain in my shoulder and leg had gone, to be replaced by a deep numbness. I could sense I was about to lose consciousness. I began to slip off the log. But the grips on my clothes tightened.

"Hang on, John!" came Cookie's voice. "We're nearly there!"

Then the log lurched as the end ran aground on the mud. I found myself momentarily floating free, before being dragged up across the bank.

"Well well," murmured a Scottish voice that I recognized. "So, you survived after all, Lieutenant."

"Thanks to Private Parker, " I said.

With that I was lifted up on to a stretcher and carried off. As I was taken away, I managed to lift my right hand in a thumbs-up to Cookie, Ba Maung, Tig Kyan and Private Parker. In the faint moonlight I saw them all smile back at me.

We had done it. We'd completed our mission. And we'd made it back home.

THE 1943 CHINDIT CAMPAIGN

Of the 3,000 Chindits who went into Burma in February 1943, about 2,000 made it back to India. During the campaign, they had travelled over 1,000 miles through treacherous jungle. In reality they were ordered to disperse and withdraw before they could carry out their objectives. However, the Chindits caused major disruptions in Burma, including cutting other supply lines to the Japanese front-line forces.

Early in 1944, the second Chindit campaign was launched, from the west, into Burma with a much larger force of 23,000 men in six brigades. At the same time, another Chindit-style guerrilla attack behind enemy lines was launched by the Americans in the north of Burma. These American guerrillas were known as Merrill's Marauders after their commander, Brigadier-General Frank Merrill. They initially attacked both by air and by jungle penetration. They were part of an overall campaign to recapture Burma, combined with traditional frontal assaults by British, American and Chinese troops.

Caught on all sides, the Japanese forces, under General Mutaguchi, fought hard to defend their positions. But on 8 July 1944, General Mutaguchi ordered their retreat. Additional British, American and Chinese forces were poured in as the Allied offensive increased. By February 1945, Allied forces had taken most of Burma. The capital, Rangoon, was finally taken by units of General Messervy's British IV Corps on 6 May 1945. This signalled the end of the war in Burma.

Orde Wingate himself was killed at the start of the second Chindit campaign when his B-25 bomber crashed into the Burmese jungle on 24 March 1944.

WHAT HAPPENED NEXT?

The Long Range Penetration offensive into Burma by Wingate's Chindits had a threefold effect:

• It showed that British troops could defeat the Japanese in jungle fighting, something that had been considered impossible. The military establishment had previously seen the Japanese as invincible in this area of combat.

• It persuaded the reluctant Americans to put more military resources into a future guerrilla campaign in Burma, which, in fact, took place in 1944.

• It led to the Japanese bringing more of their forces into Burma to oppose similar attacks, so weakening their defences elsewhere on the Pacific front. Japanese leaders later admitted that this factor contributed heavily to their defeat.